Published by Patrick Cameron Limited

My Bridal Hair Album
"for your perfect day"

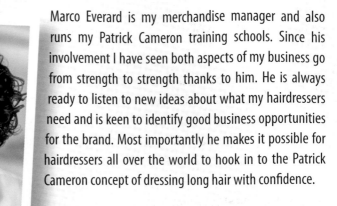

When I started my career in hairdressing, I was inspired by the fact that it was in my power to transform a women just by dressing her hair. My goals were simple, I wanted to be a success in what I did, travel the world, and be respected in my industry - Today I believe I have achieved all of these.

This year I celebrate 20 years of working in my own business, mainly internationally and often in collaboration with Wella who are a truly global company. I would like to thank Wella for their continued support and friendship over this period, not only here in Europe but throughout the world. I have always believed in them and support their unwavering dedication to education. I consider this to be a major reason for our success together and I hope that we as a team can continue to inspire the world's stylists for many more years to come.

As I look back on an amazing career, I would like to take this opportunity to pay tribute to a few people who are close to me and who make my world a better place to work in. Firstly, my business partner, Sue Callaghan, who for the past 18 years has been my corner stone both in business and my personal life. She deals with my hectic schedules, work assignments, contracts, finances and customer relations etc. She shares my vision of dedication and excellence to the hairdressing industry and continuously supports me in my creative work and also my training.

Most of all she keeps me on an even keel and without her support I know I wouldn't be in the respected position that I am in today.

Marco Erbi, is my Artistic Director and helps me look after the creative side of my international shows. One of the very special and unique things that he does for me is to hand make all the costumes that my models wear on stage. It can take him up to 9 months to design and make some of his most amazing couture creations and his reputation for originality has become his trademark. Marco is one of the most imaginative people I know, I can show my ideas to him and then he works his own magic to support my concept for a show. He also assists me back stage and in my training schools. He is my right hand man and he travels around the world with me which is a great comfort – he is the person, that creatively, I respect most.

Marco Everard is my merchandise manager and also runs my Patrick Cameron training schools. Since his involvement I have seen both aspects of my business go from strength to strength thanks to him. He is always ready to listen to new ideas about what my hairdressers need and is keen to identify good business opportunities for the brand. Most importantly he makes it possible for hairdressers all over the world to hook in to the Patrick Cameron concept of dressing long hair with confidence.

I would like to take this opportunity to thank the Wella global family for the memories, the laughs, the unbelievable experience but most of all for the many lifelong friends that I have made along the way. I would like to say thank-you so much for your respect and support over the past 20 years.

There are many more people that I have met along the way that I would also like to thank but the list is so long – I think they know who they are from the warmth and respect I give them when we meet.

The long hair market continues to grow, yet the number of salons who specialise in this area are few. In this book I take my readers back to the basics of dressing hair for one of the most important events in a women's life, her wedding day. I invite you to take away some of my ideas and techniques and use them to develop your salon business.

Over the past 20 years I have been asked on numerous occasions where I get my creativity and inspiration from. The answer is not so simple.

I am often inspired by a place I have visited, or a movie I have seen or maybe just from looking at the work of a young hairdressing student. There will be something different that will attract my interest, maybe something subliminal but quite often it is just the people that surround me in my wonderful career.

I have found that the more you share your ideas with other people the more room you make for creativity.

Enjoy and remember it is in your power to transform that bride, she will thank you for it.

Patrick Cameron

4

Introduction

Foreword

When Patrick approached me to write the foreword for his new book, I asked myself what the three things are which make him stand out as a stylist and as a business partner. Wella Professionals have had the privilege of working closely with Patrick for 20 years now.

Firstly, it is the outstanding quality of his training. All of his seminars for Wella Professionals and System Professional are consistently fully booked. The reason behind this is clear when you see Patrick in action. Stylists leave the sessions feeling confident and armed to bring a whole host of new looks back to the salon. If there is one thing that hasn't changed over the years, it is the exceptional feedback Patrick receives from the audience. He never fails to inspire, enthuse and delight.

Secondly, Patrick has remained down to earth despite his stunning career and his undeniable status as a hairdressing and media darling. Revered around the world for his up-styling skills, as a long-hair expert, Patrick has always remained grounded and true.

Last but not least, hairdressers around the world not only love his dazzling personality, but also his unique way of spreading the spark of inspiration among stylists. He is a truly passionate hairdresser, and this is what unites him with Wella Professionals – his unconditional passion for hair.

These characteristics make him ideally suited for writing a book like this. He is one of the very few stylists with the ability to create styles that brides dream of. This liberates her individual beauty and creates the magical moment we call Hair Triumph. Patrick is a once in a lifetime talent who understands how to achieve exactly this.

For the future, Wella Professionals and I personally look forward to continuing on the incredible journey to delighting and inspiring the world's stylists for many years to come – together and passionately professional.

Alexander Herzberg
Global Education Leader
P&G Salon Professional

Contents

*Hold ponytail
firm to scalp
and place
closed grip*

*Place grips through both
ends of Patrick Cameron
hair tie*

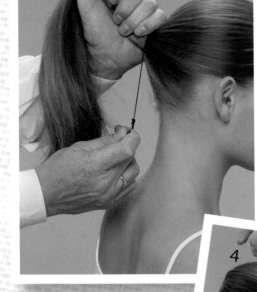

3

Place second grip under hair tie

*Pull tight around
and around
ponytail*

Step 1
- Haarklemmen durch beide Enden des Haargummis von Patrick Cameron stecken
- Inserire le forcine alle due estremità dell'elastico Patrick Cameron
- Colocar horquillas en ambos extremos de la goma Patrick Cameron
- Placer les fixe-mèches à travers les deux extrémités de l'attache pour cheveux Patrick Cameron

Step 2
- Pferdeschwanz fest am Kopf festhalten und geschlossene Haarklemme anbringen
- Tenere saldamente l'estremità della coda vicina alla cute e sistemare una forcina chiusa
- Sujetar la coleta con firmeza en el cuero cabelludo y colocar una horquilla cerrada
- Maintenir fermement la queue de cheval au cuir chevelu et placer la barrette

Step 3
- Fest anziehen und um den Pferdeschwanz herum fest anziehen
- Avvolgere più volte intorno alla coda di cavallo
- Enrollar tirando con fuerza de la coleta
- Bien tirer tout autour de la queue

Step 5
- Zweite Haarklemme unter Haargummi anbringen
- Sistemare una seconda forcina sotto la coda di cavallo
- Colocar una segunda horquilla debajo de la goma
- Placer un second fixe-mèches sous l'attache pour cheveux

Pony Tail Technique

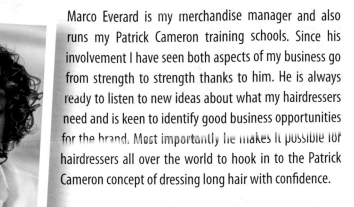

When I started my career in hairdressing, I was inspired by the fact that it was in my power to transform a women just by dressing her hair. My goals were simple, I wanted to be a success in what I did, travel the world, and be respected in my industry - Today I believe I have achieved all of these.

This year I celebrate 20 years of working in my own business, mainly internationally and often in collaboration with Wella who are a truly global company. I would like to thank Wella for their continued support and friendship over this period, not only here in Europe but throughout the world. I have always believed in them and support their unwavering dedication to education. I consider this to be a major reason for our success together and I hope that we as a team can continue to inspire the world's stylists for many more years to come.

As I look back on an amazing career, I would like to take this opportunity to pay tribute to a few people who are close to me and who make my world a better place to work in. Firstly, my business partner, Sue Callaghan, who for the past 18 years has been my corner stone both in business and my personal life. She deals with my hectic schedules, work assignments, contracts, finances and customer relations etc. She shares my vision of dedication and excellence to the hairdressing industry and continuously supports me in my creative work and also my training.

Most of all she keeps me on an even keel and without her support I know I wouldn't be in the respected position that I am in today.

Marco Erbi, is my Artistic Director and helps me look after the creative side of my international shows. One of the very special and unique things that he does for me is to hand make all the costumes that my models wear on stage. It can take him up to 9 months to design and make some of his most amazing couture creations and his reputation for originality has become his trademark. Marco is one of the most imaginative people I know, I can show my ideas to him and then he works his own magic to support my concept for a show. He also assists me back stage and in my training schools. He is my right hand man and he travels around the world with me which is a great comfort – he is the person, that creatively, I respect most.

Marco Everard is my merchandise manager and also runs my Patrick Cameron training schools. Since his involvement I have seen both aspects of my business go from strength to strength thanks to him. He is always ready to listen to new ideas about what my hairdressers need and is keen to identify good business opportunities for the brand. Most importantly he makes it possible for hairdressers all over the world to hook in to the Patrick Cameron concept of dressing long hair with confidence.

I would like to take this opportunity to thank the Wella global family for the memories, the laughs, the unbelievable experience but most of all for the many lifelong friends that I have made along the way. I would like to say thank-you so much for your respect and support over the past 20 years.

There are many more people that I have met along the way that I would also like to thank but the list is so long – I think they know who they are from the warmth and respect I give them when we meet.

The long hair market continues to grow, yet the number of salons who specialise in this area are few. In this book I take my readers back to the basics of dressing hair for one of the most important events in a women's life, her wedding day. I invite you to take away some of my ideas and techniques and use them to develop your salon business.

Over the past 20 years I have been asked on numerous occasions where I get my creativity and inspiration from. The answer is not so simple.

I am often inspired by a place I have visited, or a movie I have seen or maybe just from looking at the work of a young hairdressing student. There will be something different that will attract my interest, maybe something subliminal but quite often it is just the people that surround me in my wonderful career.

I have found that the more you share your ideas with other people the more room you make for creativity.

Enjoy and remember it is in your power to transform that bride, she will thank you for it.

Patrick Cameron

4

Introduction

My Bridal Hair Album
"for your perfect day"

1

Place grips through both ends of Patrick Cameron hair tie

2

Hold ponytail firm to scalp and place closed grip

5

4

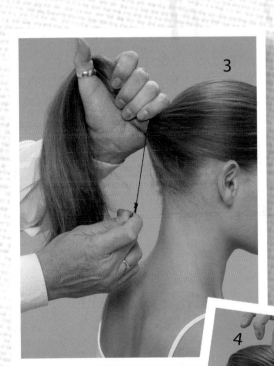

3

Pull tight around and around ponytail

Place second grip under hair tie

6

Pony Tail Technique

Step 1
- Haarklemmen durch beide Enden des Haargummis von Patrick Cameron stecken
- Inserire le forcine alle due estremità dell'elastico Patrick Cameron
- Colocar horquillas en ambos extremos de la goma Patrick Cameron
- Placer les fixe-mèches à travers les deux extrémités de l'attache pour cheveux Patrick Cameron

Step 2
- Pferdeschwanz fest am Kopf festhalten und geschlossene Haarklemme anbringen
- Tenere saldamente l'estremità della coda vicina alla cute e sistemare una forcina chiusa
- Sujetar la coleta con firmeza en el cuero cabelludo y colocar una horquilla cerrada
- Maintenir fermement la queue de cheval au cuir chevelu et placer la barrette

Step 3
- Fest anziehen und um den Pferdeschwanz herum fest anziehen
- Avvolgere più volte intorno alla coda di cavallo
- Enrollar tirando con fuerza de la coleta
- Bien tirer tout autour de la queue

Step 5
- Zweite Haarklemme unter Haargummi anbringen
- Sistemare una seconda forcina sotto la coda di cavallo
- Colocar una segunda horquilla debajo de la goma
- Placer un second fixe-mèches sous l'attache pour cheveux

Foreword

When Patrick approached me to write the foreword for his new book, I asked myself what the three things are which make him stand out as a stylist and as a business partner. Wella Professionals have had the privilege of working closely with Patrick for 20 years now.

Firstly, it is the outstanding quality of his training. All of his seminars for Wella Professionals and System Professional are consistently fully booked. The reason behind this is clear when you see Patrick in action. Stylists leave the sessions feeling confident and armed to bring a whole host of new looks back to the salon. If there is one thing that hasn't changed over the years, it is the exceptional feedback Patrick receives from the audience. He never fails to inspire, enthuse and delight.

Secondly, Patrick has remained down to earth despite his stunning career and his undeniable status as a hairdressing and media darling. Revered around the world for his up-styling skills, as a long-hair expert, Patrick has always remained grounded and true.

Last but not least, hairdressers around the world not only love his dazzling personality, but also his unique way of spreading the spark of inspiration among stylists. He is a truly passionate hairdresser, and this is what unites him with Wella Professionals – his unconditional passion for hair.

These characteristics make him ideally suited for writing a book like this. He is one of the very few stylists with the ability to create styles that brides dream of. This liberates her individual beauty and creates the magical moment we call Hair Triumph. Patrick is a once in a lifetime talent who understands how to achieve exactly this.

For the future, Wella Professionals and I personally look forward to continuing on the incredible journey to delighting and inspiring the world's stylists for many years to come – together and passionately professional.

Alexander Herzberg
Global Education Leader
P&G Salon Professional

Contents

Introduction

1

2

3

*Brush into S - shape and
hold with index fingers*

4

5

6

*Hold S - shaped wave with
butterfly clip*

Repeat

7

8

Step 3
- In S-Form bürsten und mit Zeigefingern festhalten
- Con la spazzola formare un'onda a S e trattenerla con l'indice
- Cepillar en forma de S y sujetar con los dedos índice
- Brosser en forme de S et maintenir avec les index

Step 4
- S-förmige Welle mit Schmetterlingsklammer (Butterfly-Clip)befestigen
- Fermare l'onda a S con una clip a farfalla
- Sujetar la onda en forma de S con una pinza de mariposa
- Maintenir la vague en forme de S en utilisant une barrette papillon

Step 5
- Wiederholen
- Ripetere
- Repetir
- Répéter le mouvement

Step 7
- Auf der gegenüberliegenden Seite wiederholen
- Ripetere sul lato opposto
- Repetir en el otro lado
- Répéter le mouvement du côté opposé

Repeat on opposite side

Elegant Waves

Place mousse on hands and work gently into hair

Product:
Use System
Professional Super
Mousse

Distribute mousse evenly with wide tooth comb

Diffuser dry

Step 1
- Mousse auf die Hände geben und leicht in das Haar einarbeiten
- Prendere un po' di mousse e passarla delicatamente sui capelli con le mani
- Ponerse espuma en las dos manos y aplicarla suavemente en el cabello
- Mettre un peu de mousse dans les mains et la faire pénétrer doucement dans les cheveux

Step 3
- Mousse gleichmäßig mit weitzahnigem Kamm verteilen

- Distribuire la mousse uniformemente con un pettine a denti larghi
- Distribuir uniformemente la espuma con un peine de púas anchas
- Répartir la mousse uniformément avec un peigne à larges dents

Step 4
- Mit Diffuser trocknen
- Asciugare con diffusore
- Secar con difusor
- Sécher au diffuseur

Natural Curly Hair – Diffuser Dry

Create horizontal section. Wind around Babyliss conical wand

Repeat higher up head

Brush through gently

<u>Tip</u>

Take large sections when creating ringlets

Step 1
- Horizontale Partie abstecken. Um konischen Lockenstab von Babyliss wickeln
- Creare una sezione orizzontale. Arricciare con Babyliss
- Crear una sección horizontal. Enrollar alrededor del cono Babyliss
- Créer une partie horizontale. Enrouler autour d'un fer à boucler Babyliss

Step 3
- Weiter höher am Kopf wiederholen
- Ripetere in un punto più alto della testa
- Repetir subiendo por la cabeza
- Répéter le mouvement plus haut sur la tête

Step 6
- Leicht durchbürsten
- Spazzolare delicatamente
- Cepillar todo suavemente
- Brosser délicatement la chevelure

Red Carpet Waves

Section below crown

Backcomb roots

Crisscross grips along section

Overlay top section

Fit comb under grips

Veil Technique

Step 1
- Partie unterhalb des Oberkopfes
- Sezione sotto la corona
- Partir por debajo de la coronilla
- Partie sous le dessus de tête

Step 2
- Haaransatz toupieren
- Cotonare alle radici
- Cardar las raíces
- Crêper les racines

Step 3
- Haarklemmen entlang der Haarpartie kreuzweise befestigen
- Incrociare le forcine lungo la sezione

- Entrecruzar horquillas a lo largo de la sección
- Entrecroiser les fixe-mèches le long de la partie

Step 4
- Obere Haarpartie darüber legen
- Ricoprire la sezione superiore
- Superponer la parte superior
- Recouvrir la partie de dessus

Step 5
- Kamm unter Haarklemmen befestigen
- Inserire il pettine sotto le forcine
- Peinar debajo de las horquillas
- Placer le peigne sous les fixe-mèches

Gisela style 1

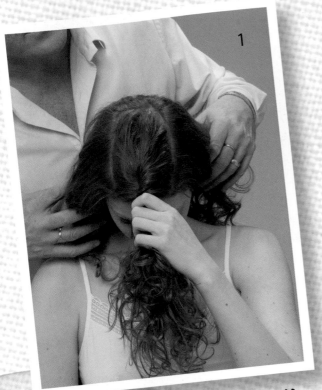

1

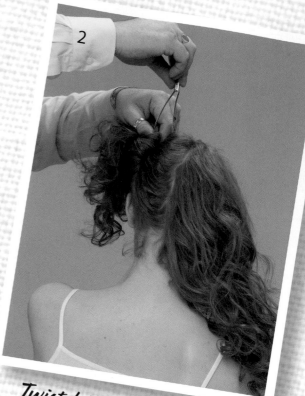

2

Take large rectangular section
and hold away

Twist left side and section
clip away

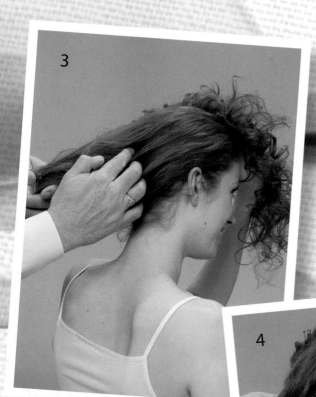

3

Gently pull back and
divide into two

4

5

Create a soft 2 strand braid
(see also pictures 6 - 10)

Gisela style 1

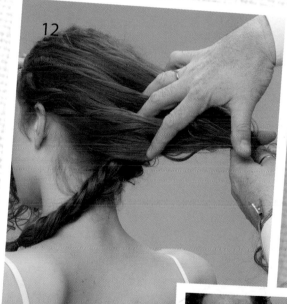

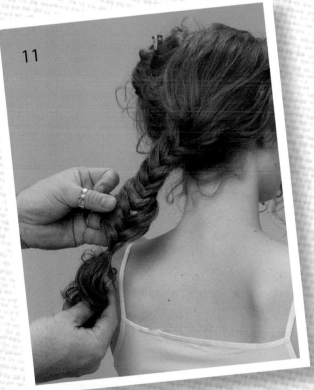

Loose braid finished with a
Patrick Cameron end elastic

Repeat on left

Gisela style 1

*Pull gently at braid
from end elastic
to head*

*Pull gently at
braid from
head to end
elastic*

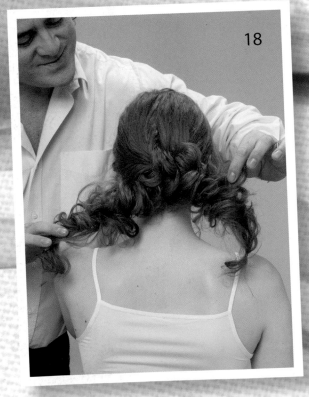

Repeat on other side

Gisela style 1

*Pull back and grip vertically
to scalp*

20

Tip

The two braids must cross over each other

21

Repeat on other side

Crisscross braids

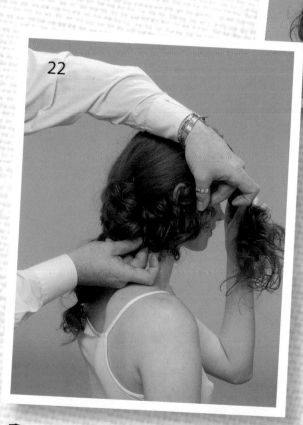

22

23

24

Drape over grips, grip to hold and repeat on other side

Drape top gently over towards back

Gisela style 1

13

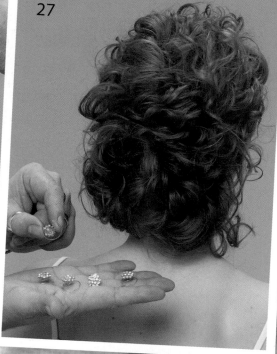

*Twist and grip tails
in to match texture*

Tip

*Place finished textured braids
in a horseshoe shape over
scalp grips*

*Decorate with Patrick Cameron
accessories*

Step 1
- Große rechteckige Haarpartie abteilen und vom Kopf weg halten
- Separare una grande sezione rettangolare
- Tomar una gran sección rectangular y separarla
- Prendre une grande partie rectangulaire et maintenir à part

Step 2
- Linke Seite drehen und Haarpartie mit Clips seitlich feststecken
- Attorcigliare il lato sinistro e fermare con una clip
- Enrollar la parte izquierda y separar con un pinza de peluquería
- Torsader le côté gauche et attacher la partie à part

Step 3
- Leicht nach hinten ziehen und in zwei Teile unterteilen
- Tirare leggermente indietro e dividere in due
- Tirar suavemente hacia atrás y dividir en dos
- Tirer doucement vers l'arrière et séparer en deux

Step 5
- Aus 2 Haarsträhnen einen weichen Zopf flechten
- Creare una treccia morbida con due ciocche
- Crear una trenza suelta con 2 mechones
- Créer une tresse souple à 2 mèches

Step 11
- Locker geflochtenen Zopf mit einem Patrick Cameron Haargummi abschließen
- Legare la treccia con un elastico Patrick Cameron
- Acabar la trenza suelta con una goma Patrick Cameron
- Tresse souple attachée avec un élastique de finition Patrick Cameron

Step 12
- Auf der linken Seite wiederholen
- Ripetere a sinistra
- Repetir en la izquierda
- Répéter le mouvement à gauche

Step 14
- Vom Haargummi aus zum Kopf hin leicht am Zopf ziehen
- Pizzicare leggermente la treccia dall'elastico alla testa

- Tirar suavemente de la trenza desde la goma hasta la cabeza
- Tirer doucement sur la tresse de l'élastique vers la tête

Step 16
- Vom Kopf zum Haargummi hin leicht am Zopf ziehen
- Pizzicare leggermente la treccia dalla testa all'elastico
- Tirar suavemente de la trenza desde la cabeza hasta la goma
- Tirer doucement sur la tresse de la tête vers l'élastique

Step 18
- Auf der anderen Seite wiederholen
- Ripetere sul lato opposto
- Repetir al otro lado
- Répéter de l'autre côté

Step 19
- Nach hinten ziehen und mit Klammer senkrecht am Kopf befestigen
- Tirare indietro e fissare verticalmente
- Tirar hacia atrás y sujetar en vertical al cuero cabelludo
- Tirer en arrière et fixer verticalement au cuir chevelu

Step 20
- Auf der anderen Seite wiederholen
- Ripetere sul lato opposto
- Repetir al otro lado
- Répéter de l'autre côté

Step 21
- Zöpfe kreuzweise übereinander legen
- Incrociare le trecce
- Entrecruzar las trenzas
- Entrecroiser les tresses

Step 22
- Über den Klammern drapieren, mit Klammern feststecken, um ihnen Halt zu geben, und auf der anderen Seite wiederholen
- Coprire le forcine, fisssare e ripetere sull'altro lato
- Disponer por encima de las horquillas, sujetar y repetir en el otro lado
- Draper sur les fixe-mèches, fixer pour maintenir en place et répéter le mouvement de l'autre côté

Step 24
- Das Haar oben sanft nach hinten über drapieren
- Modellare la zona superiore

- Disponer la parte superior suavemente por encima hacia atrás
- Draper le dessus légèrement au-dessus vers l'arrière

Step 26
- Drehen und Enden mit Klammer feststecken, so dass sie zur Textur passen
- Avvolgere e fissare le ciocche creando texture
- Enrollar y sujetar las colas para combinar con la textura
- Torsader et fixer les queues en texture égale

Step 27
- Mit Patrick Cameron Accessoires schmücken
- Decorare con gli accessori Patrick Cameron
- Decorar con accesorios Patrick Cameron
- Décorer avec des accessoires Patrick Cameron

Gisela style 1

Alexa style 1

1

Create large rectangular section

2

Asymmetric ponytail at occipital

3

Divide ponytail into 3 sections

4

5

Grip 2cm from base

Alexa style 1

Product:
Use SP Pearl Smooth
to add shine
and hold

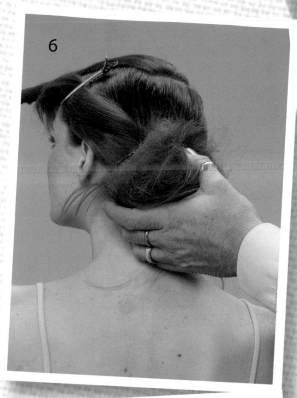

6

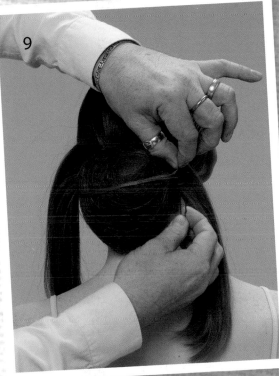

9

7

8

Shape a round ball

10

11

Repeat

12

Take fine strands over shape
and grip

Tip

Make strands flat
and smooth like
a thin
ribbon

Alexa style 1

13

Place right section up and over

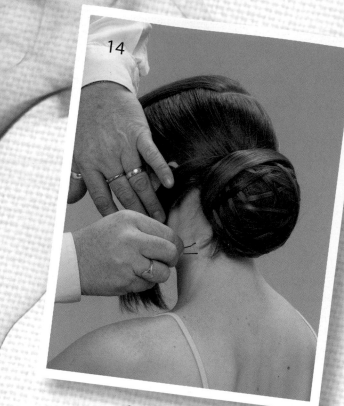

14

Grip to hold

15

Place left section under and
around and grip

16

17

Backcomb
gently to roots

Alexa style 1

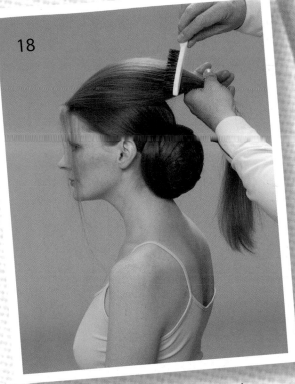

18

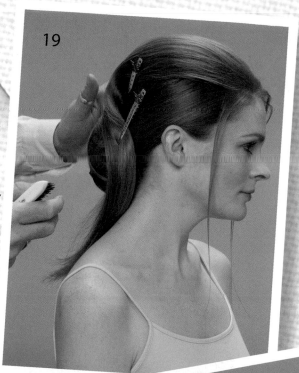

19

Use Patrick Cameron section clips for placement

Smooth gently back

Step 1
- Große rechteckige Haarpartie abteilen
- Creare un'ampia sezione rettangolare
- Crear una gran sección rectangular
- Créer une grande partie rectangulaire

Step 2
- Asymmetrischer Pferdeschwanz am Hinterkopf
- Queue de cheval asymétrique au niveau de l'occipital
- Coleta asimétrica en el occipital
- Utiliser les pointes pour former une décoration

Step 3
- Pferdeschwanz in 3 Haarpartien unterteilen
- Dividir la coleta in 3 seccioni
- Dividir la coleta en 3 secciones
- Séparer la queue en 3

Step 4
- 2 cm vom Ansatz her mit Klammer befestigen
- Fissare a 2 cm dalla base
- Sujetar a 2 cm de la base
- Fixer avec des pinces 2cm à partir de la base

Step 6
- Eine runde Kugel formen
- Creare una forma rotonda
- Formar un moño redondo
- Créer une forme ronde

Step 9
- Feine Strähnen über die Form legen und mit Klammer befestigen
- Coprire con le ciocche la forma e la forcina
- Llevar mechones finos sobre la forma y sujetar
- Prendre de fines mèches, les mettre sur la forme et fixer

Step 10
- Wiederholen
- Ripetere
- Repetir
- Répéter le mouvement

Step 13
- Rechte Haarpartie nach oben und darüber legen
- Ricoprire la forma con la sezione destra
- Colocar la sección derecha hacia arriba y por encima
- Placer la partie droite vers le haut et au-dessus

Step 14
- Mit Klammer befestigen, um Halt zu geben
- Fermare con una forcina
- Sujetar con horquillas
- Fixer pour maintenir en place

Step 15
- Linke Haarpartie darunter und drum herum legen und mit Klammer befestigen
- Portare la sezione sinistra sotto e intorno alla forma e fissare
- Colocar la sección izquierda debajo y alrededor y sujetar
- Placer la partie gauche vers le bas et autour et fixer

Step 16
- Leicht bis zum Haaransatz toupieren
- Cotonare delicatamente le radici
- Cardar suavemente hasta la raíz
- Crêper doucement aux racines

Step 18
- Leicht nach hinten glätten
- Lisciare leggermente
- Alisar suavemente hacia atrás
- Lisser légèrement l'arrière

Step 19
- Nehmen Sie Patrick Cameron Haarclips, um das Haar zu arrangieren
- Utilizzare i clip Patrick Cameron per fissare
- Utilizar pinzas de peluquería Patrick Cameron para sujetar
- Utiliser les pinces séparation mèches Patrick Cameron pour placer la coiffure

Step20
- Das Ende drum herum und darunter befestigen
- Ripiegare la coda
- Meter la cola alrededor y debajo
- Rentrer la queue autour et dessous

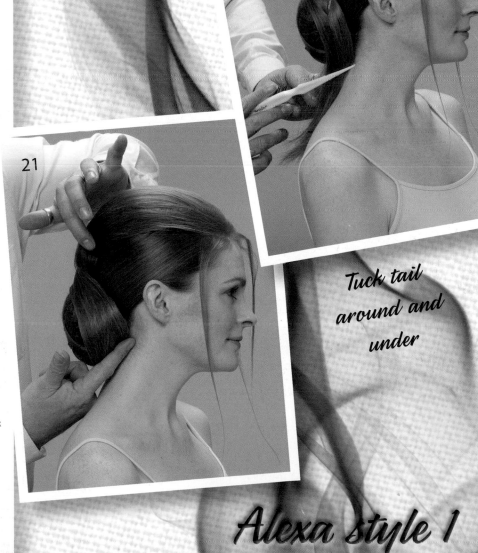

20

21

Tuck tail around and under

Alexa style 1

Holly style 1

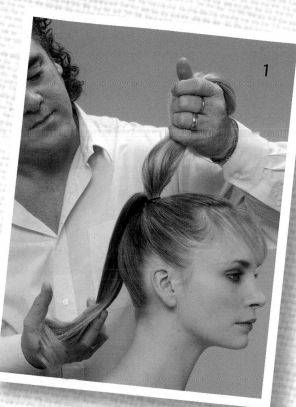

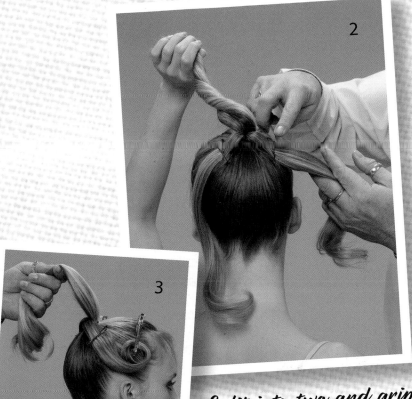

**Ponytail at crown,
leaving soft fringe**

**Split into two and grip
2cm from base**

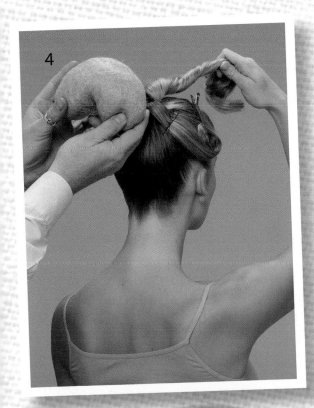

Patrick Cameron hair pad

Shape into a crescent and grip to scalp

Holly style 1

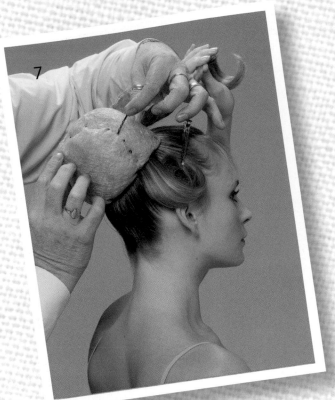

Grip second pad to first

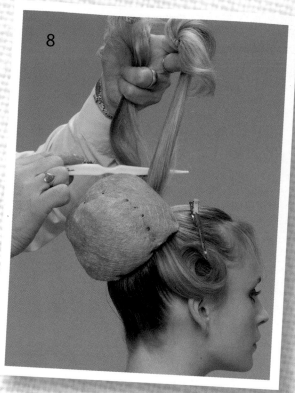

Divide top section into two

Drape right section over pad

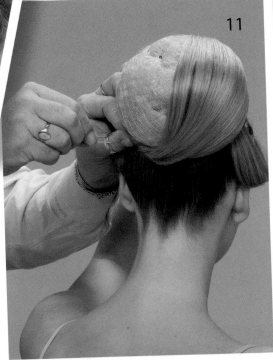

Tip

Round brush blow dry for a smooth, even finish.

Twist tails and tuck under

Holly style 1

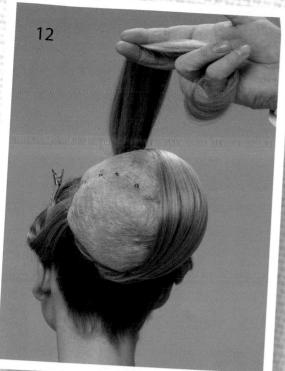

12

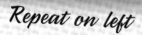

Repeat on left

13

14

15

16

17

18

19

Crisscross tails to cover ponytail base

20

Step 1
- Pferdeschwanz am Oberkopf, sanften Pony belassen
- Coda in corrispondenza della corona con frangia morbida
- Hacer una coleta en la coronilla, dejando un flequillo suelto
- Queue de cheval sur le dessus de tête, laisser une frange douce

Step 2
- In zwei Teile unterteilen und 2cm vom Ansatz mit Klammer befestigen
- Dividere in due e fissare a 2 cm dalla base
- Dividir en dos y sujetar a 2cm de la base
- Séparer en deux et fixer à 2 cm de la base

Step 4
- Patrick Cameron Hair Pad
- Crespo Patrick Cameron
- Postizo Patrick Cameron
- Boudin Patrick Cameron

Step 5
- Zu einer Sichel formen und mit einer Klammer am Kopf befestigen
- Creare una forma a mezzaluna e fissare
- Formar una media luna y sujetar al cuero cabelludo
- Former en croissant et fixer au cuir chevelu

Step 7
- Zweites Pad mit einer Klammer am ersten befestigen
- Fissare il primo crespo al secondo
- Sujetar el segundo postizo al primero
- Fixer un deuxième boudin au premier

Step 8
- Oberste Haarpartie in zwei Teile unterteilen
- Dividere la sezione superiore in due.
- Dividir en dos la sección superior
- Séparer la partie de dessus en deux

Step 9
- Rechte Haarpartie über das Pad drapieren
- Modellare la sezione destra per coprire i crespi

- Disponer la sección superior sobre el postizo
- Draper la partie droite au-dessus du boudin

Step 11
- Enden drehen und darunter stecken
- Avvolgere le code e ripiegarle
- Enrollar las colas y meterlas debajo
- Torsader les queues et rentrer dessous

Step 12
- Auf der linken Seite wiederholen
- Ripetere a sinistra
- Repetir en la izquierda
- Répéter à gauche

Step 17
- Enden kreuzweise so legen, dass der Ansatz des Pferdeschwanz des verdeckt wird
- Incrociare le code per ricoprire la base della coda di cavallo
- Entrecruzar las colas para cubrir la base de la coleta
- Entrecroiser les queues pour recouvrir la base de la queue de cheval

Holly style 1

Caroline style 1

1

*Section ear to behind
crown to ear*

2

*Low ponytail at occipital. 2 x
Patrick Cameron hair pads*

Tip

*Make sections
smooth and perfect.
Take time to get
it right!*

3

Join pads with grips

4

*Roll ponytail up
around pads*

5

Caroline style 1

Fold into crescent and grip
at scalp

Remove a 3cm
rectangular section
and leave

Brush over to left and
grip vertically

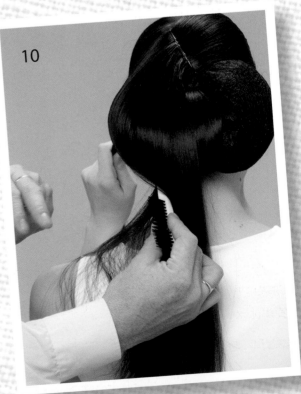

Place over ¹/₂ of shape.
Tuck tails under pad

Caroline style 1

11

12

Twist tails

Grip

13

14

15

Repeat on opposite side

16

17

18

Caroline style 1

Drape top over to cover grips

Tuck tail under pad

Decorate with Patrick Cameron accessories

Step 1
- Haarpartie vom Ohr bis hinter den Oberkopf bis zum Ohr
- Creare una sezione sotto la corona tra le due orecchie
- Dividir desde la oreja hasta la mitad de la coronilla a ambos lados
- Partie oreille vers l'arrière du dessus de tête vers l'oreille

Step 2
- Pferdeschwanz unten am Hinterkopf. 2 x Patrick Cameron Hair Pads
- Formare una coda bassa in corrispondenza della regione occipitale. 2 crespi Patrick Cameron
- 3 Hacer una coleta baja en el occipital. 2 postizos Patrick Cameron
- Queue de cheval basse au niveau de l'occipital. 2 boudins Patrick Cameron

Step 3
- Pads mit Haarklammern verbinden
- Unire I crespi con le forcine
- Unir los postizos con horquillas
- Assembler les boudins à l'aide de fixe-mèches

Step 4
- Pferdeschwanz um Pads nach oben rollen
- Avvolgere la coda di cavallo intorno ai crespi
- Enrollar la coleta alrededor de los postizos
- Enrouler la queue de cheval autour des boudins

Step 6
- Sichelförmig anlegen und am Kopf mit Klammer befestigen
- Piegare a mezzaluna e fissare sulla base
- Doblar en forma de media luna y sujetar al cuero cabelludo
- Plier en forme de croissant et fixer sur le cuir chevelu

Step 7
- Eine rechteckige Haarpartie von 3 cm lösen und hängen lassen
- Separare una sezione rettangolare di 3 cm
- Retirar una sección rectangular de 3cm y soltar
- Enlever une partie rectangle de 3 cm et laisser de côté

Step 9
- Zur linken Seite hin bürsten und senkrecht mit einer Klammer befestigen
- Spazzolare verso sinistra e fermare verticalmente

- Cepillar hacia la izquierda y sujetar en vertical
- Brosser sur le dessus vers la gauche et fixer verticalement

Step 10
- Über die Hälfte der Form legen. Enden unter Pad stecken
- Coprire metà della forma. Nascondere le code sotto i crespi
- Colocar encima de ½ forma. Meter las colas debajo del postizo
- Placer sur ½ de la forme. Rentrer les queues sous le boudin

Step 11
- Enden drehen
- Intrecciare le code
- Enrollar las colas
- Torsader les queues

Step 12
- Mit Klammer befestigen
- Fermare con una forcina
- Sujetar
- Fixer

Step 13
- 6 Auf der gegenüberliegenden Seite wiederholen
- Ripetere sul lato opposto
- Repetir en el otro lado
- Répéter le mouvement du côté opposé

Step 19
- 2 Das obere Haar darüber drapieren, um die Klammern zu verdecken
- Modellare la parte superiore per coprire le forcine
- Disponer la parte superior por encima para tapar las horquillas
- Draper dessus pour recouvrir les fixe-mèches

Step 20
- 3 Ende unter Pad stecken
- Nascondere la coda sotto i crespi
- Meter la cola debajo del postizo
- Rentrer la queue sous le boudin

Step 21
- 7 Mit Patrick Cameron Accessoires schmücken
- Decorare con gli accessori Patrick Cameron
- Decorar con accesorios Patrick Cameron
- Décorer avec des accessoires Patrick Cameron

Caroline style 1

Stephanie style 1

1

Create triangular section, temple to temple and back to occipital. Ponytail at nape

2

3

Tip

Use <u>Large</u> hot rollers

4

Fine hairnet over backcombed ponytail

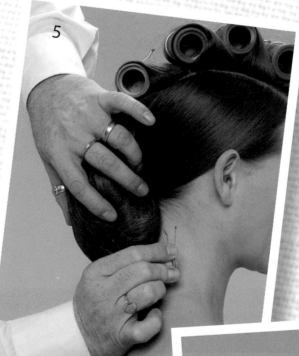

5

Create a ball shape

6

Stephanie style 1

Drape widely over shape

Repeat. Use closed grips to hold

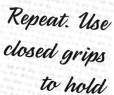

Drape waves on top of pad and grip

Continue draping to cascade waves

Stephanie style 1

12

13

Product:
Use SP Pearl Smooth
and SP Deep
Reflect

Backcomb to roots for extra lift

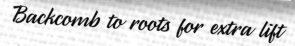

14

*Decorate with
Patrick Cameron
spiral accessories*

15

Step 1
- Dreieckige Haarpartie abteilen, von Schläfe zu Schläfe und hinten bis zum Hinterkopf. Pferdeschwanz am Nackenansatz
- Creare una sezione triangolare, tra le due tempie e sul retro in corrispondenza della regione occipitale. Coda di cavallo sulla nuca
- Crear una sección triangular, de sien a sien, y detrás hasta el occipital. Hacer una coleta en la nuca
- Créer une partie triangulaire, de tempe à tempe et de l'arrière vers l'occipital. Queue de cheval en nuque

Step 4
- Feines Haarnetz über toupierten Pferdeschwanz
- Retina sulla coda cotonata
- Colocar una redecilla fina sobre la coleta cardada
- Fine résille sur la queue de cheval crêpée

Step 5
- Zu einer Kugel formen
- Creare una forma rotonda
- Crear un moño
- Créer une forme ronde

Step 7
- Weit über die Form drapieren
- Modellare sulla forma creata
- Disponer el cabello suelto sobre la forma
- Draper dans un mouvement large sur la forme

Step 9
- Wiederholen. Geschlossene Klammern verwenden, um Halt zu geben

- Ripetere. Fissare con forcine chiuse
- Repetir. Utilizar clips cerrados para sujetar
- Répéter. Utiliser les barrettes pour maintenir

Step 10
- Wellen oben auf dem Pad drapieren und mit Klammer befestigen
- Modellare in onde all'estremità superiore del crespo e fissare
- Disponer ondas sobre la parte superior del postizo y sujetar
- Draper les vagues sur le dessus du boudin et fixer

Step 11
- Weiter zu kaskadenartigen Wellen drapieren
- Continuare a modellare in onde sovrapposte
- Seguir disponiendo las ondas en cascada
- Continuer à draper en une cascade de vagues

Step 12
- Am Haaransatz toupieren, um dem Haar zusätzliches Volumen zu verleihen
- Cotonare alle radici per donare maggior volume
- Cardar hasta la raíz para una fijación extra
- Crêper aux racines pour un effet très bombé

Step 14
- Mit spiralenförmigen Accessoires von Patrick Cameron schmücken
- Decorare con gli accessori con base spirale Patrick Cameron
- Decorar con accesorios espirales Patrick Cameron
- Décorer avec des accessoires en spiral Patrick Cameron

Stephanie style 1

Gergana style 1

1

2

3

Spray for extra hold

4

Hot roller entire head

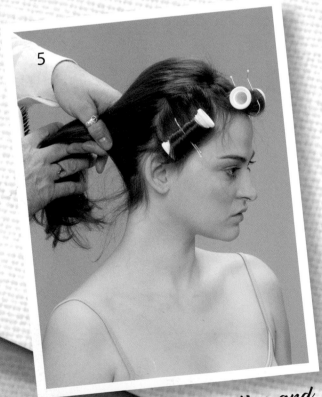

5

6

Loose weave front section and
hot roller

Weave section from ear to ear

Gergana style 1

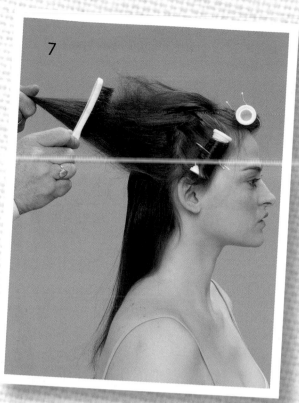

Gently backcomb top section

Twist and grip to hold

Backcomb tail loosely

Patrick Cameron hair pad

Roll tail over hair pad firmly

Gergana style 1

Spread evenly over pad to create bouffant

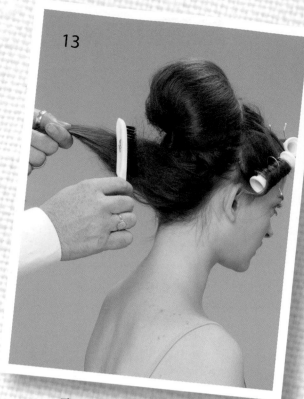

Backcomb loosely

Twist under pad and grip

Backcomb tail

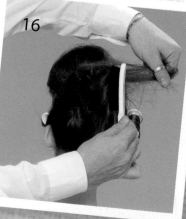

Gergana style 1

17

Smooth tail

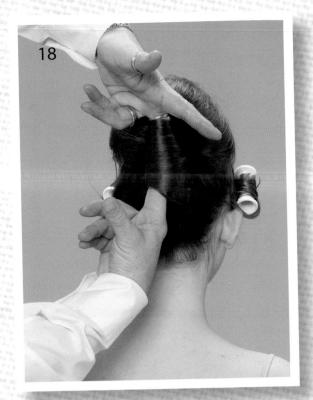

18

Create roll

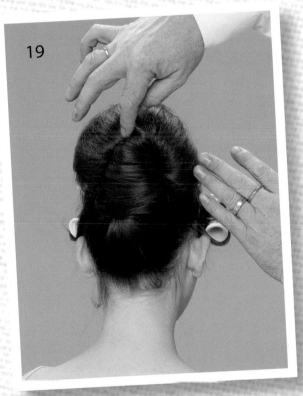

19

Grip roll to back of bouffant

20

Twist back and grip to bouffant

Gergana style 1

Drape loosely over side and repeat on opposite side

Drape front loosely

Decorate with Patrick Cameron accessories

Gergana style 1

Step 1
- Spray auftragen, um Extrahalt zu geben
- Spray per tenuta forte
- Aplicar spray para una fijación extra
- Laquer pour une tenue extra forte

Step 2
- Große Rolle (Hot Roller) auf dem ganzen Kopf
- Applicare i bigodini riscaldanti a tutta la testa
- Utilizar rulos calientes en toda la cabeza
- Mettre des bigoudis chauffants sur toute la tête

Step 5
- Vordere Haarpartie lose flechten und große Rolle (Hot Roller)
- Sezionare a zig-zag e applicare i bigodini riscaldanti
- Unir suavemente la sección frontal y colocar rulos calientes
- Tresse souple sur le devant et bigoudis chauffants

Step 6
- Haarpartie von Ohr zu Ohr flechten
- Separare a zig-zag una sezione da un orecchio all'altro
- Unir la sección de oreja a oreja
- Tresser la partie d'oreille à oreille

Step 7
- Obere Haarpartei leicht toupieren
- Cotonare leggermente la sezione superiore
- Cardar suavemente la sección superior
- Crêper doucement la partie de dessus

Step 8
- Drehen und mit Klammer befestigen, um Halt zu geben
- Attorcigliare e fissare con forcine
- Enrollar y sujetar
- Torsader et fixer pour maintenir en place

Step 9
- Ende locker toupieren
- Cotonare delicatamente la coda

- Cardar suavemente la cola
- Crêper légèrement la queue

Step 10
- Patrick Cameron Hair Pad
- Crespo Patrick Cameron
- Postizo Patrick Cameron
- Boudin Patrick Cameron

Step 11
- Ende fest über Hair Pad rollen
- Arrotolare la coda sul crespo
- Enrollar la cola sobre el postizo firmemente
- Enrouler fermement la queue au-dessus du boudin

Step 12
- Gleichmäßig über Pad verteilen, so dass die füllige Form einer Hochsteckfrisur entsteht
- Distribuire sul crespo per creare un vaporoso bouffant
- Distribuir uniformemente sobre el postizo para crear un ahuecado
- Etaler les cheveux régulièrement sur le boudin pour créer un effet bouffant

Step 13
- Locker toupieren
- Cotonare leggermente
- Cardar suavemente
- Crêper souplement

Step 14
- Unter Pad drehen und mit Klammer befestigen
- Avvolgere sotto il crespo e fissare
- Enrollar bajo el postizo y sujetar
- Torsader sous le boudin et fixer

Step 15
- Ende toupieren
- Cotonare la coda
- Cardar la cola
- Crêper la queue

Step 17
- Ende glätten
- Lisciare la coda
- Alisar la cola
- Lisser la queue

Step 18
- Rolle anlegen
- Creare una forma rotonda
- Crear un rodete
- Créer un rouleau

Step 19
- Rolle hinten an der fülligen Form einer Hochsteckfrisur mit Klammer befestigen
- Fissare la forma rotonda sul retro del bouffant
- Sujetar el rodete a la parte trasera del ahuecado
- Fixer le rouleau à l'arrière du bouffant

Step 20
- Nach hinten drehen und mit Klammer an der fülligen Form einer Hochsteckfrisur befestigen
- Avvolgere e fissare al bouffant
- Enrollar hacia atrás y unir al ahuecado
- Torsader à l'arrière et fixer avec des pinces au bouffant

Step 21
- Locker über die Seite drapieren und auf der gegenüberliegenden Seite wiederholen
- Modellare leggermente ai lati e ripetere sul lato opposto
- Disponer el cabello suelto sobre el lateral y repetir en el otro lado
- Draper souplement sur le côté et répéter de l'autre côté

Step 22
- Vorne locker drapieren
- Modellare la sezione anteriore
- Disponer la parte frontal suelta
- Draper le devant souplement

Step 23
- Mit Patrick Cameron Accessoires schmücken
- Decorare con gli accessori Patrick Cameron
- Decorar con accesorios Patrick Cameron
- Décorer avec des accessoires Patrick Cameron

Ella style 1

1

2

3

Large rectangular section on top.
Ponytail to crown. Hot roller all

Remove 3 small sections
from ponytail and hold with
section clips

4

5

Place 2 fingers
under and roll
up to barrel curl

Take section from ponytail, twist
and pull at twist to texturise

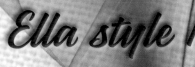
Ella style 1

Tip

Texture : When twisting to
right, pull texture out on
right. When twist to left,
pull texture out on left

6

7

Repeat 5 times around ponytail

Grip at base

9

8

10

11

Remove 3 small sections

Ella style 1

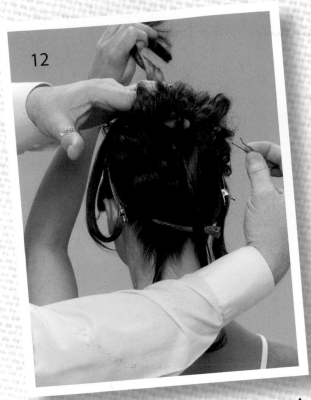

12

Divide remaining sections into fine strands and randomly place over shape

13

Place 3 more textured barrel curls on top

14

15

16

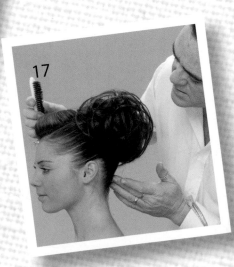

17

Spray gently to place each strand

Ella style 1

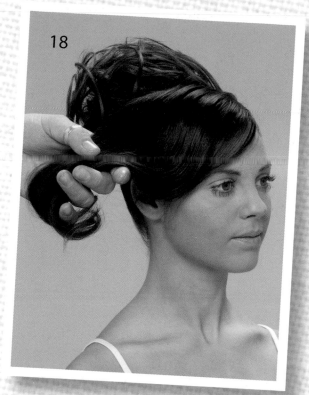

18

19

Gently drape to side

20

Spray and diffuser dry

Step 1
- Große rechteckige Haarpartie oben. Pferdeschwanz zum Oberkopf. Große Rolle (Hot Roller)
- Larga sezione rettangolare sul davanti. Coda di cavallo alla corona. Applicare i bigodini riscaldanti
- Crear una sección rectangular grande en la parte superior. Hacer una coleta en la coronilla. Rulos calientes en todo.
- Grande partie rectangulaire sur le dessus. Queue de cheval sur le dessus de tête. Poser des bigoudis chauffants

Step 3
- 3 kleine Partien aus dem Pferdeschwanz lösen und mit Haarspangen festhalten
- Prendere 3 piccole sezioni dalla coda e fermarle con clip
- Separar 3 secciones pequeñas de la coleta y sujetar con pinzas de peluquería
- Enlever les 3 petites parties de la queue de cheval et maintenir avec des pinces séparation mèches

Step 4
- Eine Partie aus dem Pferdeschwanz nehmen, drehen und in der Drehung ziehen, um ihr die richtige Textur zu geben.
- Prendere una sezione dalla coda, intrecciarla e modellarla per donare texture.
- Coger una sección de la coleta, enrollarla tirando de ella para darle textura.
- Prendre une partie de la queue de cheval, torsader et tirer au niveau de la torsade pour créer la texture.

Step 5
- Mit 2 Fingern darunter greifen und zu einer Barrel-Locke aufrollen
- Con due dita formare un boccolo
- Colocar 2 dedos debajo y enrollar hacia arriba para crear ondas
- Placer 2 doigts dessous et enrouler vers le haut pour former une grosse bouche

Step 6
- Am Ansatz mit einer Klammer befestigen
- Fermare alla base
- Sujetar en la base
- Fixer à la base

Step 7
- Um dem Pferdeschwanz herum 5 Mal wiederholen
- Ripetere 5 volte intorno alla coda
- Repetir 5 veces alrededor de la coleta
- Répéter le mouvement 5 fois autour de la queue de cheval

Step 11
- Drei kleine Haarpartien lösen
- Prendere 3 piccole sezioni
- Separar 3 secciones pequeñas
- Enlever les 3 petites parties

Step 12
- Drei Barrel-Locken, denen eine stärkere Textur gegeben wurde, oben anordnen
- Formare altri tre boccoli sulla parte superiore
- Colocar 3 ondas más texturizadas en la parte superior
- Placer 3 grosses bouches plus texturées sur le dessus

Step 13
- Die restlichen Haarpartien in feine Strähnen unterteilen und willkürlich über der Form anordnen
- Dividere le sezioni rimanenti in piccole ciocche e distribuire a caso sull'acconciatura
- Dividir las demas secciones en mechones finos y colocarlos aleatoriamente sobre la forma
- Séparer les autres parties en fines mèches et les étaler au hasard sur la forme

Step 15
- Um jeder Strähne festen Halt zu geben, leicht Spray auftragen
- Fissare con lo spray ogni ciocca
- Aplicar spray suavemente para fijar cada mechón
- Laquer légèrement pour placer chaque mèche

Step 18
- Vorsichtig zur Seite hin drapieren
- Modellare delicatamente sul lato
- Disponer suavemente a un lado
- Draper légèrement sur le côté

Step 20
- Spray auftragen und mit Diffuser trocknen
- Rifinire con spray e diffusore
- Aplicar spray y secar con difusor
- Laquer et sécher au diffuseur

Ella style 1

Katkin style 1

1

2

3

Backcomb 2cm root area

4

5

6

7

Catch back tails loosely and twist

Tip

Allow time for hot rollers to cool to achieve a firm set

Grip to hold

Katkin style 1

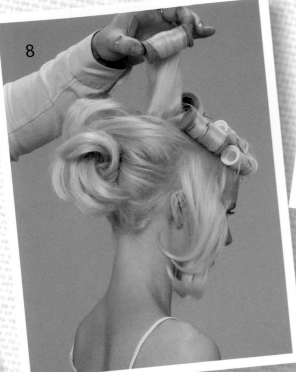

8

9

10

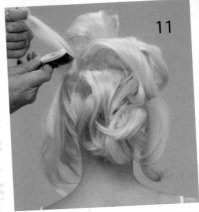

11

*Repeat on top and drape
back softly*

12

Twist sides back firmly

13

Grip

Product:
SP Ultimation

Katkin style 1

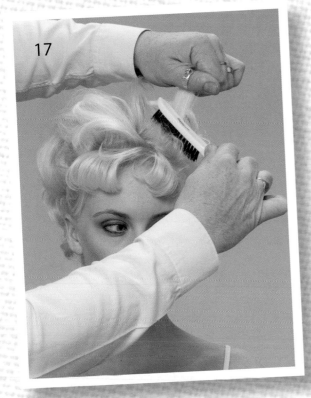

Backcomb roots

Spray and diffuser dry

Step 3
- Vom Ansatz her 2 cm toupieren
- Cotonare a 2 cm dalla radice
- Cardar 2cm hasta la raíz
- Crêper les racines sur 2 cm

Step 6
- Die hinteren Enden locker fassen und drehen
- Formare code morbide e avvolgere
- Coger las colas traseras suavemente y enrollar
- Saisir à l'arrière les queues souplement et torsader

Step 7
- Mit Klammer befestigen, um ihnen Halt zu geben
- Fermare con una forcina
- Sujetar
- Fixer pour maintenir en place

Step 8
- Oben wiederholen und sanft nach hinten drapieren
- Ripetere sul davanti e modellare delicatamente i capelli
- Repetir en la parte superior y disponer hacia atrás suavemente
- Répéter le mouvement sur le dessus de tête et draper à l'arrière en donnant un mouvement voluptueux

Step 12
- Die Seiten fest nach hinten drehen
- Avvolgere i capelli sui lati
- Enrollar los laterales hacia atrás con firmeza
- Torsader fermement les côtés arrière

Step 13
- Mit Klammer befestigen
- Fermare con una forcina
- Sujetar
- Fixer

Step 17
- Haaransätze toupieren
- Cotonare le radici
- Cardar las raíces
- Crêper les racines

Step 18
- Spray auftragen und mit Diffuser trocknen
- Rifinire con spray e diffusore
- Aplicar spray y secar con difusor
- Laquer et sécher au diffuseur

Ideal for short layered hair

Katkin style 1

Gisela style 2

1

2

*Take section from
left temple to
right of neck*

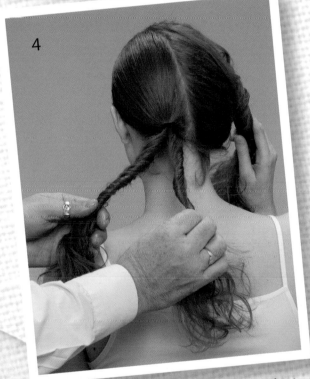

3

*Place ponytail at nape, divide
into two and twist to left*

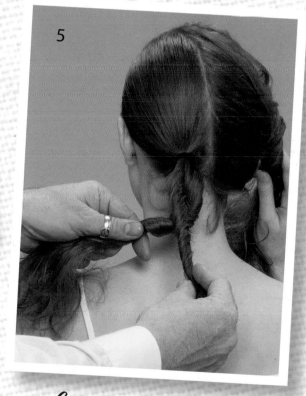

4

Twist second section to left

5

Cross right under left

Tip

*Important – do not
twist tightly.
Hold tail end
and pull up
toward base to
create texture*

Gisela style 2

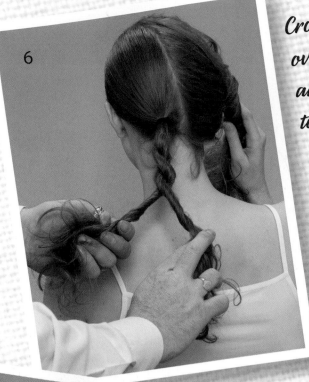

6

7

Cross left over right and continue to bottom

Finish with Patrick Cameron end elastic

8

Take right triangular section

9

Divide into two

10

Twist both to left

Gisela style 2

11

12

13

Repeat roping technique, each
time adding in a new section
from front

14

15

16

17

Starting at end elastic, pull
gently at rope

18

Gisela style 2

19

20

Repeat

21

22

*Smooth with
brush and
grip in a
semi- circle*

23

*Place tail into a
horseshoe and grip*

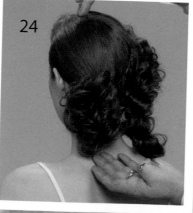

24

25

Cover grips with roped section

Gisela style 2

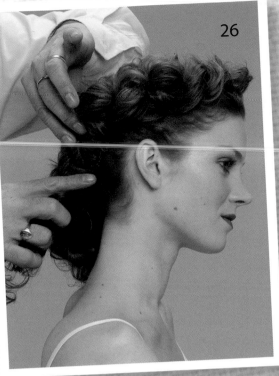

26

Grip behind ear

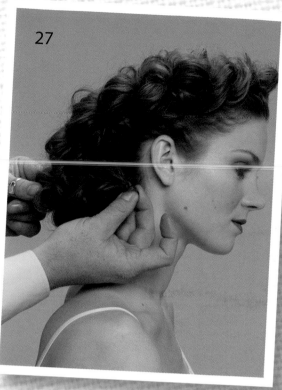

27

Grip side tail into horseshoe shape

28

Decorate with Patrick Cameron accessories

Gisela style 2

Step 1
- Von der linken Schläfe eine Haarpartie nehmen und nach rechts vom Nacken legen
- Prendere una sezione dalla tempia sinistra alla parte destra del collo
- Tomar una sección desde la sien izquierda hasta la parte derecha del cuello
- Prendre une partie de la tempe gauche vers la droite du cou

Step 3
- Pferdeschwanz am Nackenansatz platzieren, in zwei Teile unterteilen und nach links drehen
- Fare una coda sulla nuca, dividerla in due e avvolgere a sinistra
- Hacer una coleta en la nuca, dividir en dos y enrollar hacia la izquierda
- Placer la queue de cheval en nuque, séparer en deux et torsader à gauche

Step 4
- Zweite Haarpartie nach links drehen
- Avvolgere la seconda sezione a sinistra
- Enrollar la segunda sección hacia la izquierda
- Torsader une deuxième partie vers la gauche

Step 5
- Rechte Partie quer unter die linke Partie legen
- Incrociare la sezione destra sotto la sinistra
- Cruzar la parte derecha debajo de la izquierda
- Croiser la droite sous la gauche

Step 6
- Linke Partie quer über die rechte Partie legen, und so bis zum Ende fortfahren
- Incrociare la sezione sinistra sopra la destra e continuare fino in fondo
- Cruzar la parte izquierda por encima de la derecha y seguir hasta abajo
- Croiser la gauche sur la droite et continuer vers le bas

Step 7
- Zum Schluss mit einem Patrick Cameron Haargummi befestigen

- Fermare con l'elastico Patrick Cameron
- Acabar con una goma Patrick Cameron
- Terminer avec des élastiques de finition Patrick Cameron

Step 8
- Rechts dreieckige Haarpartie abteilen
- Prendere a destra una sezione triangolare
- Tomar una sección triangular a la derecha
- Prendre la partie triangulaire droite

Step 9
- In zwei Teile unterteilen
- Dividere in due
- Dividir en dos
- Séparer en deux

Step 10
- Beide nach links drehen
- Avvolgere le due sezioni a sinistra
- Enrollar las dos partes hacia la izquierda
- Torsader les deux vers la gauche

Step 11
- Flechttechnik wiederholen, wobei Sie jedes Mal von vorne eine neue Haarpartie hinzufügen
- Ripetere questa tecnica " a fune", aggiungendo ogni volta una nuova sezione dal davanti
- Repetir la técnica de enrollado añadiendo cada vez una nueva sección de la parte frontal
- Répéter la technique de tresse, chaque fois en ajoutant une nouvelle partie de devant

Step 17
- Am Haargummi beginnend, sanft an dem geflochtenen Zopf ziehen
- Iniziando dall'elastico, pizzicare leggermente la fune
- Empezando en la goma, tirar suavemente del cabello enrollado
- En commençant au niveau de l'élastique de finition, tirer doucement sur la tresse

Step 19
- Wiederholen
- Ripetere
- Repetir
- Répéter le mouvement

Step 22
- Mit der Bürste glätten und in einem Halbkreis mithilfe einer Klammer befestigen
- Lisciare con la spazzola e fermare un semicerchio
- Alisar con el cepillo y sujetar en semicírculo
- Lisser avec la brosse et fixer en demi-cercle

Step 23
- Das Ende hufeisenförmig anordnen und mit einer Klammer befestigen
- Formare una base a forma di ferro di cavallo e fissare con le forcine
- Colocar la cola en una herradura y sujetar
- Placer la queue dans un fer à cheval et fixer

Step 25
- Haarklammern mit der geflochtenen Haarpartie verdecken
- Ricoprire le forcine con la sezione lavorata a fune
- Tapar las horquillas con la sección enrollada
- Recouvrir les fixe-mèches avec la partie tressée

Step 26
- Hinter dem Ohr mit Klammer feststecken
- Fissare dietro l'orecchio
- Sujetar detrás de la oreja
- Fixer derrière l'oreille

Step 27
- Seitliches Ende hufeisenförmig mit Klammer befestigen
- Fissare la coda laterale sulla base a ferro di cavallo
- Sujetar la cola lateral en forma de herradura
- Fixer sur le côté la queue en forme de fer à cheval

Step 28
- Mit Patrick Cameron Accessoires schmücken
- Decorare con gli accessori Patrick Cameron
- Decorar con accesorios Patrick Cameron
- Décorer avec des accessoires Patrick Cameron

Alexa style 2

1

Take large
rectangular
section

2

Create triangular section
behind crown to behind ear

3

Brush both sides back into
a ponytail

4

5

Tip
Keep casual and
soft for a
younger look

Alexa style 2

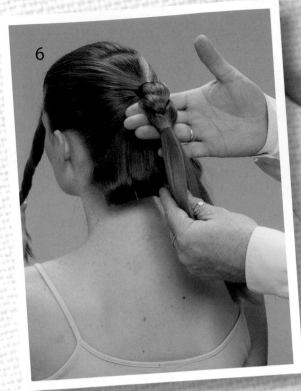

6

7

Plait down 4cmc and finish with Patrick Cameron end elastic

Pull plait up to crown and grip

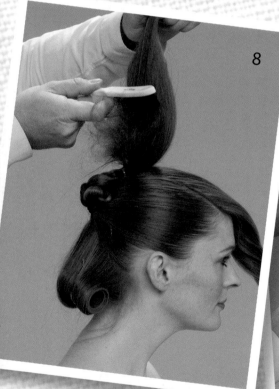

8

9

10

Divide ponytail into 3 sections

Patrick Cameron Hair Pad

Roll back over pad

Alexa style 2

Create half moon shape and
grip to scalp

Arrange loosely
to cover pad

Twist top section gently

Use brush tail to lift front

Alexa style 2

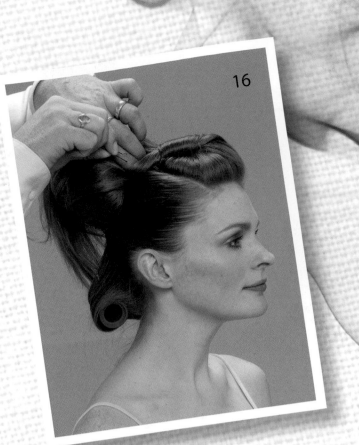

16

Grip to base

17

Backcomb gently

18

19

*Grip vertically along
middle of shape*

*A great
hairstyle
for tiara
and veil*

Alexa style 2

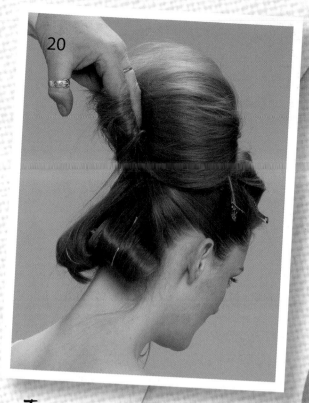

Twist tails into a loose pleat

Grip

Decorate with Patrick Cameron accessories

Step 1
- Große rechteckige Haarpartie abteilen
- Creare un'ampia sezione rettangolare
- Tomar una gran sección rectangular
- Prendre une grande partie rectangle

Step 2
- Hinter dem Oberkopf bis hinter das Ohr eine dreieckige Haarpartie abteilen
- Creare una sezione triangolare dalla corona fino alle orecchie
- Crear una sección triangular detrás de la coronilla hasta detrás de la oreja
- Créer un triangle derrière le dessus de tête à l'arrière des oreilles

Step 3
- Beide Seiten nach hinten zu einem Pferdeschwanz bürsten
- Formare una coda con la spazzola
- Cepillar ambos lados hacia atrás y hacer una coleta
- Brosser les deux côtés vers l'arrière et réaliser une queue de cheval

Step 6
- Über eine Länge von 4 cm nach unten flechten und mit einem Patrick Cameron Haargummi abschließen
- Formare una treccia di 4 cm e chiuderla con l'elastico Patrick Cameron
- Trenzar hacia abajo 4cm y terminar con una goma Patrick Cameron
- Tresser le bas sur 4cmc et fixer avec un élastique de finition Patrick Cameron

Step 7
- Den Zopf bis zum Oberkopf hoch ziehen und mit Klammer befestigen
- Portare la treccia sulla corona e fissare con una forcina
- Tirar de la trenza hacia arriba hasta la coronilla y sujetar
- Tirer la tresse vers le haut sur le dessus de tête et fixer

Step 8
- Locker toupieren
- Cotonare leggermente

- Cardar suavemente
- Crêper souplement

Step 9
- Patrick Cameron Hair Pad
- Crespo Patrick Cameron
- Postizo Patrick Cameron
- Boudin Patrick Cameron

Step 10
- Über das Pad nach hinten rollen
- Avvolgere sul crespo
- Enrollar hacia atrás sobre el postizo
- Enrouler l'arrière sur le boudin

Step 11
- Halbmondförmig anlegen und mit Klammer am Kopf befestigen
- Creare una forma a mezzaluna e fissare
- Crear una forma de media luna y sujetar al cuero cabelludo
- Créer une forme demi lune et fixer au cuir chevelu

Step 12
- Locker arrangieren, um das Pad zu verdecken
- Modellare delicatamente per ricoprire il crespo
- Disponer el cabello suelto para cubrir el postizo
- Arranger les cheveux dans un mouvement souple pour recouvrir le boudin

Step 14
- Die oberste Haarpartie leicht drehen
- Attorcigliare delicatamente la sezione superiore
- Enrollar la sección superior suavemente
- Torsader souplement la partie de dessus

Step 15
- Nehmen Sie den Bürstenstiel, um das Haar vorne anzuheben
- Utilizzare la coda della spazzola per dare volume alla parte frontale
- Cepillar la cola para elevar la parte frontal

- Utiliser le manche de la brosse pour soulever le dessus

Step 16
- Mit Klammern am Ansatz befestigen
- Fissare alla base
- Sujetar a la base
- Fixer à la base

Step 17
- Leicht toupieren
- Cotonare leggermente
- Cardar suavemente
- Crêper légèrement

Step 19
- An der Mitte der Form entlang senkrecht mit Klammer befestigen
- Fissare verticalmente con le forcine a metà della forma realizzata
- Sujetar en vertical en la mitad de la forma
- Fixer verticalement le long du milieu de la forme

Step 20
- Die Enden zu einem lockeren Zopf drehen
- Attorcigliare delicatamente le ciocche
- Enrollar las colas creando una trenza suelta
- Torsader les queues en formant un pli souple

Step 21
- Mit Klammer befestigen
- Fermare con una forcina
- Sujetar
- Fixer

Step 23
- Mit Patrick Cameron Accessoires schmücken
- Decorare con gli accessori Patrick Cameron
- Decorar con accesorios Patrick Cameron
- Décorer avec des accessoires Patrick Cameron

Alexa style 2

Holly style 2

1

Take 4cm rectangular section

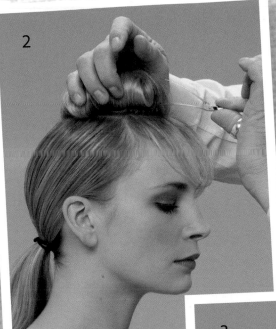

2

Place in large barrel curl

3

Brush into ponytail at nape

4

Grip Patrick Cameron hair pad into crescent shape

5

6

Holly style 2

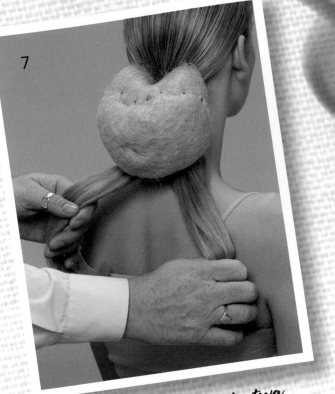

Divide ponytail into two

Smooth left section over pad, twist and grip

Hair pads give a much cleaner shape than backcombing and are easier to remove

Repeat

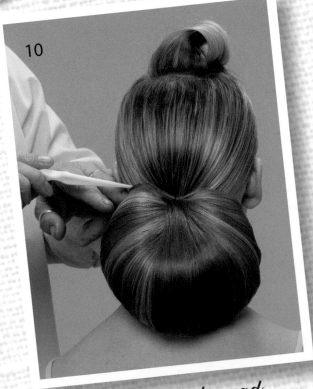

Tuck tails under pad

Holly style 2

11

12

13

Tuck tails under pad

14

Grip

Step 1
- Eine rechteckige Haarpartie von 4 cm abteilen
- Prendere una sezione rettangolare di 4 cm.
- Tomar una sección rectangular de 4cm
- Prendre une partie rectangulaire de 4cm

Step 2
- Zu einer großen Barrel-Locke drehen
- Formare un grosso boccolo
- Crear una gran onda con ella
- Placer dans une grande boucle

Step 3
- Am Nackenansatz zu einem Pferdeschwanz bürsten
- Formare con la spazzola una coda sulla nuca
- Peinar en una coleta en la nuca
- Brosser en queue de cheval au niveau de la nuque

Step 4
- Patrick Cameron Hair Pad sichelförmig mit einer Haarklammer befestigen
- Fissare un crespo Patrick Cameron in una forma a mezzaluna
- Colocar un postizo Patrick Cameron en forma de media luna
- Fixer le boudin Patrick Cameron en forme de croissant

Step 7
- Den Pferdeschwanz in zwei Teile unterteilen
- Dividere la coda in due
- Dividir la coleta en dos
- Séparer la queue de cheval en deux

Step 8
- Die linke Haarpartie glatt über das Pad ziehen, drehen und mit Klammer befestigen
- Con la sezione sinistra ricoprire il crespo, avvolgere e fissare con una forcina
- Alisar la sección izquierda sobre el postizo, enrollar y sujetar
- Lisser la partie gauche sur le boudin, torsader et fixer

Step 9
- Wiederholen
- Ripetere
- Repetir
- Répéter le mouvement

Step 10
- Die Enden unter das Pad stecken
- Nascondere le code sotto il crespo
- Meter las colas debajo del postizo
- Rentrer les queues sous le boudin

Step 13
- Die Enden unter das Pad stecken
- Nascondere le code sotto il crespo
- Meter las colas debajo del postizo
- Rentrer les queues sous le boudin

Step 14
- Mit Haarklammer befestigen
- Fermare con una forcina
- Sujetar
- Fixer

Holly style 2

Caroline style 2

1

2

3

Ponytail at crown. Create soft curls with Babyliss conical wand

4

5

Divide into 8 sections

6

Weave first left section, over and under other sections to the right

Product:

SP Ends Express on each strand

Repeat from left to right

Caroline style 2

Take tail over the first tail and drop the first tail back down beside the other 6 tails

Repeat all the way down

Place Patrick Cameron end elastic ³/₄ of the way down

Repeat technique on front section

Caroline style 2

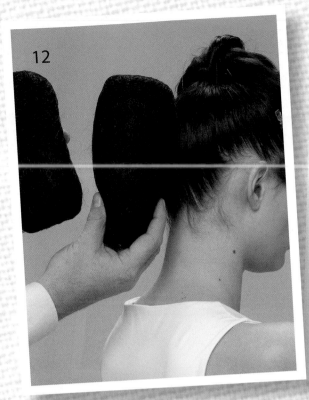

12

13

Grip pads
together and
to scalp to
create shape

14

2 x Patrick Cameron hair pads

Drape and spread
braid over pads

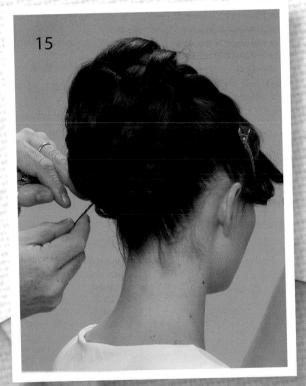

15

Tuck tails under pad
and grip

16

Drape front
braid loosely
to cover base
and grip

Caroline style 2

67

17

Grip to hold

18

Decorate with Patrick Cameron accessories

19

Caroline style 2

Step 1
- Pferdeschwanz am Oberkopf. Mit dem konischen Lockensstab von Babyliss weiche Locken herstellen
- Fare una coda in corrispondenza della corona. Creare ricci morbidi con l'arricciacapelli Babyliss
- Hacer una coleta en la coronilla. Crear unos rizos suaves con el cono Babyliss
- Une queue de cheval sur le dessus de tête. Réaliser des boucles souples avec le fer à boucler Babyliss

Step 4
- In 8 Haarpartien unterteilen
- Dividere in 8 sezioni
- Dividir en 8 secciones
- Séparer en 8 parties

Step 5
- Erste linke Partie über und unter die anderen Partien nach rechts flechten.
- Intrecciare la prima sezione a sinistra sopra e sotto le altre sezioni a destra.
- Unir la primera sección izquierda por encima y por debajo de las secciones de la derecha.
- Tresser d'abord la partie gauche, au-dessus et sous les autres parties vers la droite.

Step 6
- Von links nach rechts wiederholen
- Ripetere da sinistra a destra
- Repetir de izquierda a derecha
- Répéter de gauche à droite

Step 7
- Das Ende über das erste Ende nehmen und das erste Ende neben den anderen 6 Enden hinten nach unten fallen lassen.
- Portare la coda formata sopra la prima coda e lasciare cadere la prima coda accanto alle altre sei.
- Llevar la sección por encima de la primera cola y soltar la primera cola de atrás hacia abajo encima de las otras 6 colas.

Prendre la queue au-dessus de la première queue et laisser tomber la première queue à l'arrière à côté des 6 autres queues.

Step 8
- Bis nach unten wiederholen
- Ripetere il procedimento
- Repetir hasta abajo
- Répéter le mouvement jusqu'au bout vers le bas

Step 9
- Patrick Cameron Haargummi in ¾-Höhe von oben nach unten befestigen
- Fermare a un terzo della lunghezza con un elastico Patrick Cameron
- Colocar una goma Patrick Cameron a ¾ de distancia (hacia abajo)
- Placer l'élastique Patrick Cameron au ¾ de la fin

Step 10
- Technik bei der vorderen Haarpartie wiederholen
- Ripetere la procedura sulla sezione frontale
- Repetir la técnica en la parte frontal
- Répéter la technique sur le devant

Step 12
- 2 x Patrick Cameron Hair Pads
- 2 crespi Patrick Cameron
- 2 postizos Patrick Cameron
- 2 boudins Patrick Cameron

Step 13
- 1Pads zusammen feststecken und am Kopf so befestigen, dass eine Form entsteht
- Unire i crespi e fissarli per creare la forma di base
- Unir los postizos y cardar para dar forma
- Fixer les boudins ensemble et sur le cuir chevelu pour créer la forme

Step 14
- Den Zopf über die Pads drapieren und verteilen
- Modellare e nascondere i crespi con la treccia
- Disponer y distribuir la trenza sobre los postizos
- Draper et étaler la natte au-dessus des boudins

Step 15
- Die Enden unter einen Pad stecken und mit einer Klammer befestigen
- Raccogliere le code sotto il crespo e fissare
- Meter las colas debajo del postizo y sujetar
- Rentrer les queues sous le boudin et fixer

Step 16
- Den vorderen Zopf locker drapieren, so dass der Ansatz und die Haarklammer verdeckt sind
- Modellare in modo morbido la treccia sul davanti per coprire la base
- Disponer la trenza frontal suelta para cubrir la base y sujetar
- Draper le devant avec la tresse tout en souplesse pour recouvrir la base et fixer

Step 17
- Mit Klammer befestigen, um Halt zu geben
- Fermare con una forcina
- Sujetar con horquillas
- Fixer pour maintenir en place

Step 18
- Mit Patrick Cameron Accessoires schmücken
- Decorare con gli accessori Patrick Cameron
- Decorar con accesorios Patrick Cameron
- Décorer avec des accessoires Patrick Cameron

Stephanie style 2

Hot roller large rectangular section, temple to crown

Section off ¼ of ponytail

Grip 2cm from base and section clip pin curls to hold

Stephanie style 2

7

Place fine hairnet over to create oval shape

8

Grip first section to base

9

10

Split into two and drape over

11

Grip to hold and repeat on opposite side

Stephanie style 2

Repeat with second, third and fourth sections. Gripping and draping over.

Tip
To create ultimate hold –
Spray and diffuser dry
(high heat,
slow speed)

Release pin curls

Stephanie style 2

18

19

20

Drape to cover grips

21

Decorate with Patrick Cameron accessories

Step 1
- Große Rolle (Hot Roller) große eckige Haarpartie, von der Schläfe bis zum Oberkopf
- Applicare i bigodini riscaldanti a una larga sezione rettangolare , dalla tempia alla corona della testa
- Colocar rulos calientes grandes en una sección rectangular desde la sien hasta la coronilla
- Mettre des bigoudis chauffants sur une grande partie rectangulaire, de la tempe vers le dessus de tête

Step 2
- Vom Pferdeschwanz ¼ abteilen
- Sezione a un ¼ dalla coda di cavallo
- Separar ¼ de la coleta
- Couper ¼ de la queue de cheval

Step 4
- Mit Klammer 2 cm vom Ansatz befestigen und die feinen Locken (Pin Curls) mit einem Haarclip befestigen, um Halt zu geben
- Fissare a 2 cm dalla base e fermare i riccioli con clip
- Sujetar a 2cm de la base y utilizar pinzas de peluquería para hacer ondas y sujetarlas
- Fixer 2cm de la base et maintenir les boucles avec des pinces séparation mèches

Step 7
- Feines Haarnetz so darüber legen, dass eine ovale Form entsteht
- Coprire con una retina creando una forma ovale
- Colocar una redecilla fina por encima para crear una forma ovalada
- Enfiler la fine résille pour créer une forme ovale

Step 9
- Erste Haarpartie am Ansatz mit Klammer befestigen
- Fissare la prima sezione alla base
- Sujetar la primera sección a la base
- Fixer d'abord la partie à la base

Step 10
- In zwei Teile unterteilen und darüber drapieren
- Dividere in due e modellare
- Dividir en dos y disponer por encima
- Séparer en deux et draper par-dessus

Step 11
- Mit Klammer befestigen, um Halt zu geben, und auf der gegenüberliegenden Seite wiederholen
- Fissare e ripetere sul lato opposto
- Sujetar y repetir en el otro lado
- Fixer pour maintenir en place et répéter le mouvement du côté opposé

Step 12
- Bei der zweiten, dritten und vierten Haarpartie wiederholen. Mit Klammern befestigen und darüber drapieren.
- Ripetere con la seconda, la terza e la quarta sezione. Fissare e modellare
- Repetir con la segunda, tercera y cuarta sección. Sujetar y disponer por encima.
- Répéter avec la deuxième, troisième et quatrième partie. Fixer et draper par-dessus.

Step 17
- Feine Locken (Pin Curls) lösen
- Liberare i riccioli fissati con clip
- Soltar los clips de las ondas
- Libérer les boucles fixées avec des pinces

Step 18
- So drapieren, dass die Klammern verdeckt werden
- Modellare per coprire le forcine
- Disponer el cabello para cubrir las horquillas
- Draper pour recouvrir les fixe-mèches

Step 21
- Mit Patrick Cameron Accessoires schmücken
- Decorare con gli accessori Patrick Cameron
- Decorar con accesorios Patrick Cameron
- Décorer avec des accessoires Patrick Cameron

Stephanie style 2

Gergana style 2

1

2

Create soft curls with Babyliss
conical wand

3

Backcomb
loosely

4

Crisscross grips from ear to ear

Roll under and
grip to nape

5

6

Tip

Drape top area
loosely and casually
to create a soft
bob effect

Gergana style 2

7

8

Drop curls loosely over shape

Spray and diffuser dry (high heat, slow speed)

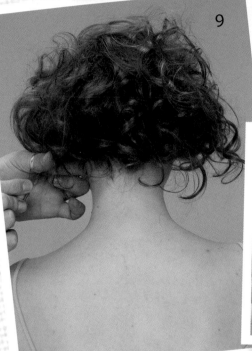

9

10

11

Grip to base to create a bob effect

12

Step 1
- Mit konischem Lockenstab von Babyliss weiche Locken herstellen
- Creare ricci morbidi con l'arricciacapelli Babyliss
- Crear unas ondas suaves con el cono Babyliss
- Créer des boucles souples avec le fer à boucler Babyliss

Step 2
- Eine Haarpartie von unterhalb der Schläfe bis zu unterhalb des Oberkopfes um den Kopf herum abteilen
- Sezione sotto la tempia fino alla sezione sotto la corona, intorno al capo
- Dividir debajo de la sien hasta debajo de la coronilla, alrededor de la cabeza
- Partie sous la tempe sous le dessus de tête, autour

de la tête

Step 3
- Von Ohr zu Ohr Haarklammern kreuzweise befestigen
- Fissare con forcine incrociate tra le due orecchie
- Entrecruzar horquillas de oreja a oreja
- Entrecroiser les fixe-mèches d'oreille à oreille

Step 4
- Locker toupieren
- Cotonare leggermente
- Cardar suavemente
- Crêper légèrement

Step 5
- Darunter rollen und im Nacken mit Klammer befestigen
- Creare una forma rotonda e fissare sulla nuca

- Enrollar debajo y sujetar a la nuca
- Enrouler dessous et fixer en nuque

Step 8
- Locken lose über die Form fallen lassen
- Coprire la forma con i ricci
- Disponer ondas sueltas sobre la forma
- Laisser tomber les boucles souplement sur la forme

Step 9
- Am Ansatz mit Klammer so befestigen, dass ein Bob-Effekt entsteht
- Fissare alla base per creare un effetto a caschetto
- Sujetar a la base para crear un efecto "bob"
- Fixer à la base pour créer un effet bob

Step 11
- Spray auftragen und mit Diffuser trocknen (hohe Hitze, niedrige Geschwindigkeit)
- Rifinire con spray e diffusore (calore massimo, velocità minima)
- Aplicar spray y secar con difusor (calor alto, velocidad baja)
- Laquer et sécher au diffuseur (chaleur forte, faible vitesse)

Step 12
- Mit Patrick Cameron Accessoires schmücken
- Decorare con gli accessori Patrick Cameron
- Decorar con accesorios Patrick Cameron
- Décorer avec des accessoires Patrick Cameron

Gergana style 2

Decorate with Patrick Cameron accessories

Ella style 2

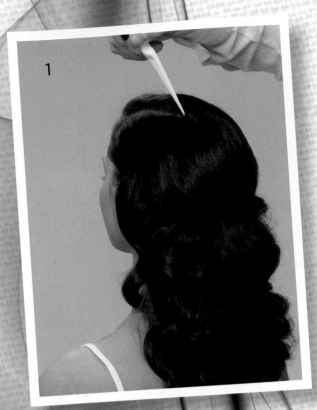

1

2

Prepare with elegant wave technique. Section from left temple to middle of neck

Tips

Hot roller preparation important (see Elegant wave technique)

3

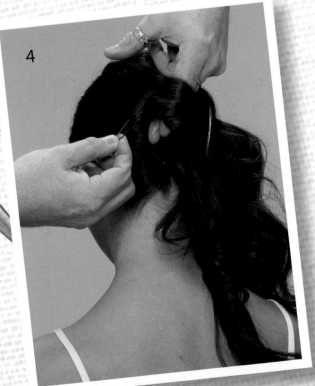

4

Crisscross grips vertically

Divide gripped section into two. Barrel curl, grip to hold and place tail

Ella style 2

78

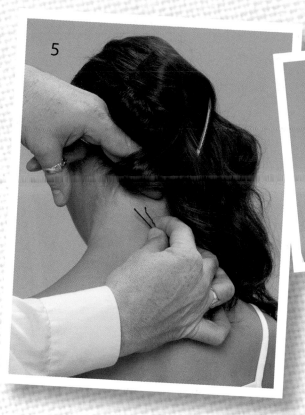

Repeat

*Remove rectangular section
from top. Brush remaining
hair back and grip behind ear*

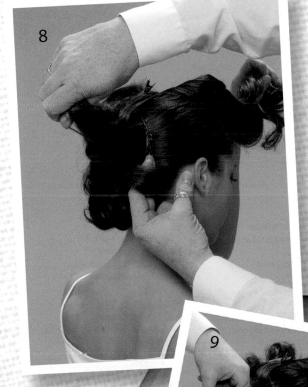

*Repeat
Barrel Curl
technique*

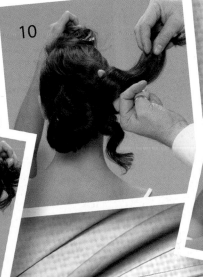

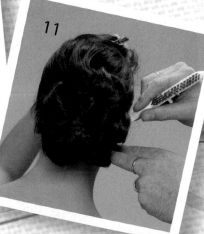

Ella style 2

Drape top loosely over side

Place butterfly clips onto waves and drape tails back

Step 1
- Mit eleganter Wellentechnik vorbereiten. Haarpartie von der linken Schläfe bis zur Nackenmitte abteilen
- Ondulare la capigliatura. Formare una sezione dalla tempia sinistra alla metà del collo.
- Preparar con la técnica de ondas elegantes. Dividir desde la sien izquierda hasta la mitad del cuello
- Préparer avec une élégante technique de vague. Partie depuis la tempe gauche vers le milieu du cou

Step 3
- Mit Klammern kreuzweise vertikal befestigen
- Disporre le forcine verticalmente incrociandole.
- Entrecruzar horquillas en vertical
- Entrecroiser les fixe-mèches verticalement

Step 4
- Die befestigte Partie in zwei Teile unterteilen. Barrel-Locke, mit Klammer das Ende festhalten und befestigen
- Dividere la sezione con le forcine applicate in due. Formare un boccolo, fermare con una forcina e modellare la coda
- Dividir la sección con horquillas en dos. Crear ondas, sujetar con horquillas y colocar la cola
- Diviser la partie fixée en deux. Former une grande boucle, fixer pour maintenir en place et placer la queue

Step 5
- Wiederholen
- Ripetere
- Repetir
- Répéter le mouvement

Step 7
- Rechteckige Partie von oben lösen. Restliches Haar nach hinten bürsten und hinter dem Ohr mit Klammer befestigen
- Liberare la sezione rettangolare in alto. Spazzolare i capelli rimanenti e fermarli dietro l'orecchio
- Retirar la sección rectangular de la parte superior. Cepillar el resto del pelo hacia atrás y sujetar detrás de la oreja
- Enlever la partie rectangulaire de dessus. Brosser les cheveux restant à l'arrière et fixer derrière les oreilles

Step 8
- Barrel-Locken-Technik wiederholen
- Ripetere la tecnica precedente
- Repetir la técnica de creación de ondas
- Répéter la technique de grande boucle

Step 12
- Das obere Haar locker über die Seite drapieren
- Modellare sui lati in modo morbido
- Disponer la parte superior suelta sobre el lateral
- Draper le dessus dans un mouvement souple sur le côté

Step 13
- Schmetterlingsklammern (Butterfly-Clips) auf den Wellen befestigen und Enden hinten drapieren
- Sistemare clip a farfalla sulle onde e modellare le ciocche
- Colocar pinza de mariposa en las ondas y disponer las colas hacia atrás
- Placer les barrettes papillon sur les vagues et draper les queues vers l'arrière

Ella style 2

Alexa style 3

Create large
rectangular section

Tip
Round brush blow
dry to ensure a
smooth and shiny
finish

Ponytail behind
crown

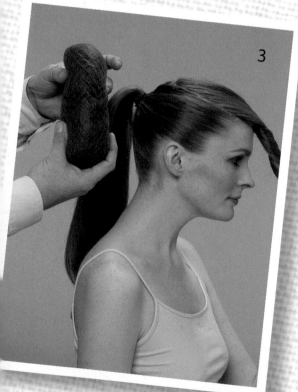

Patrick Cameron
hair pad

Roll hair pad forward

Alexa style 3

Grip to base

Shape pad in a crescent and grip to scalp

Tip

Important – Mould hair pad into an even half moon shape

Spread hair evenly over shape

Product:
SP Deep Reflect to give shine.
SP Ultimation.

Alexa style 3

Backcomb 4cm to root

Smooth back through hand
with brush

Place with Patrick Cameron
section clips

Alexa style 3

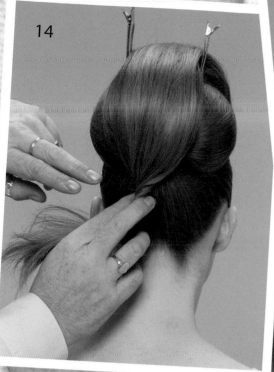

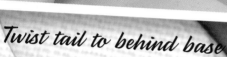
Twist tail to behind base

Twist and tuck under pad
and grip

Step 1
- Große rechteckige Haarpartie abteilen
- Creare un'ampia sezione rettangolare
- Crear una gran sección rectangular
- Créer une grande partie rectangulaire

Step 2
- Pferdeschwanz hinten am Oberkopf
- Formare una coda dietro la corona
- Hacer una coleta detrás de la coronilla
- Une queue de cheval derrière le dessus de tête

Step 3
- Patrick Cameron Hair Pad
- Crespo Patrick Cameron
- Postizo Patrick Cameron
- Boudin Patrick Cameron

Step 4
- Hair Pad nach vorne rollen
- Posizionare il crespo in avanti
- Enrollar el postizo hacia adelante
- Enrouler le boudin vers l'avant

Step 5
- Mit Klammer am Ansatz feststecken
- Fissare alla base
- Sujetar a la base
- Fixer à la base

Step 6
- Pad zu einer Sichel formen und mit Klammer am Kopf feststecken
- Formare il crespo a mezzaluna e fissare
- Dar al postizo forma de media luna y sujetar al cuero cabelludo
- Modeler le boudin en forme de croissant et fixer au cuir chevelu

Step 7
- Das Haar gleichmäßig über die Form verteilen
- Distribuire i capelli uniformemente sulla forma creata
- Distribuir el cabello uniformemente sobre la forma
- Etaler les cheveux régulièrement sur la forme

Step 9
- Das Haar 4 cm bis zum Ansatz toupieren
- Cotonare a 4 cm dalla radice
- Cardar 4cm hasta la raíz
- Crêper les racines sur 4 cm

Step 11
- Über die Hand mit der Bürste nach hinten glätten
- Lisciare con la spazzola
- Alisar hacia atrás con la mano con un cepillo
- Lisser en arrière avec une brosse

Step 12
- Mit Patrick Cameron Haarklammern anordnen
- Fissare con le clip Patrick Cameron
- Sujetar con pinzas de peluquería Patrick Cameron
- Placer avec les pinces séparation mèches Patrick Cameron

Step 14
- Ende bis hinter den Ansatz drehen
- Avvolgere ciocca fino alla base
- Enrollar la cola hasta debajo de la base
- Torsader la queue derrière la base

Step 16
- Drehen und unter dem Pad feststecken und mit Klammer befestigen
- Avvolgere ciocca e nascondere sotto il crespo e fissare
- Enrollar y meter debajo del postizo y sujetar
- Torsader et rentrer sous le boudin et fixer

Step 17
- Große Rolle (Hot Roller) und das Haar stylen
- Applicare i bigodini riscaldanti e rifinire
- Colocar rulos calientes y peinar
- Mettre des bigoudis chauffants et coiffer

Hot roller and style

Alexa style 3

85

Caroline style 3

1

3cm rectangular section back to crown

2

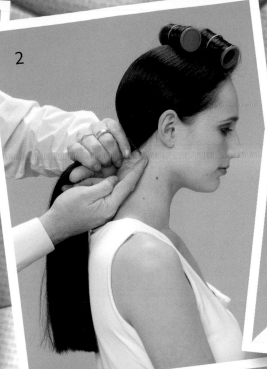

Brush into nape and grip below occipital

3

4

Use SP Polish Cream and divide into 7 sections

5

Product:
SP Polish Cream

6

Weave right section over and under the other sections

Caroline style 3

7

8

Weave left section over and under the other sections and place into a Patrick Cameron section clip

Place into a Patrick Cameron section clip

9

10

11

12

Repeat technique

Crisscross final tails and place with section clips

Tip

Great style for one length hair

Caroline style 3

Release tails and
twist both sides
upwards

Hold right side with
Patrick Cameron
section clip and grip
left to scalp

Repeat on
opposite side

Decorate with tails

Caroline style 3

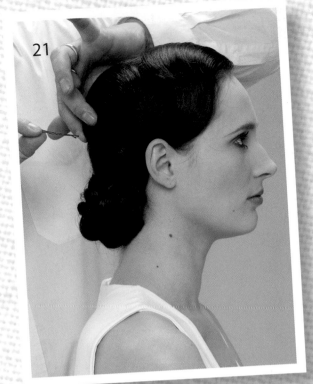

Secure wave with a closed grip across head

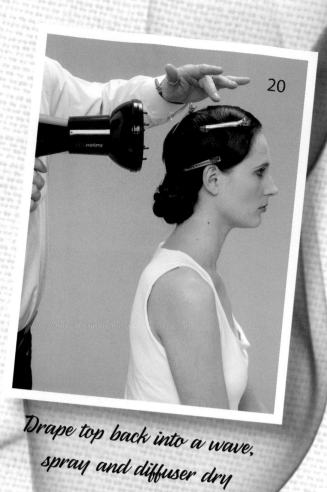

Drape top back into a wave, spray and diffuser dry

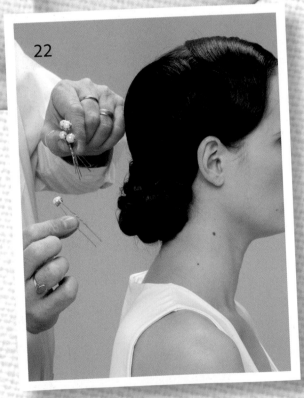

Decorate with Patrick Cameron accessories

Caroline style 3

Step 1
- Rechteckige Haarpartie von 3 cm hinten bis zum Oberkopf abteilen
- Creare una sezione rettangolare di 3 cm sul retro della testa
- Sección rectangular de 3cm detrás hasta la coronilla
- Partie rectangulaire de 3 cm à l'arrière du dessus de tête

Step 2
- Zum Nackenansatz hin bürsten und unter dem Hinterhaupt mit Haarklemme befestigen
- Raccogliere i capelli sulla nuca con la spazzola e inserire una forcina sotto la regione occipitale
- Cepillar en la nuca y sujetar debajo del occipital
- Brosser vers la nuque et fixer avec des pinces sous l'occipital

Step 4
- SP Polish Cream (Glanzcreme), um das Haar in 7 Partien zu unterteilen
- Dividere in 7 sezioni con la crema lucidante SP
- Aplicar crema SP para dividir en 7 secciones
- Appliquer de la cire SP pour séparer la chevelure en 7 parties

Step 6
- Rechte Haarpartie über und unter die anderen Partien flechten
- Intrecciare la sezione di destra sopra e sotto le altre sezioni

Step 7
- Mit einer Patrick Cameron-Haarspange (Section Clip) befestigen
- Fermare i capelli con una clip Patrick Cameron
- Colocar en un pinza de peluquería Patrick Cameron
- Placer dans une pince séparation mèches Patrick Cameron

Step 8
- Linke Haarpartie über und unter die anderen Partien flechten und mit einer Patrick Cameron-Haarspange befestigen
- Intrecciare la sezione sinistra sopra e sotto le altre sezioni e fermare i capelli con una clip Patrick Cameron
- Unir la sección izquierda por encima y por debajo de las demás secciones y colocar en un pinza de peluquería Patrick Cameron
- Tresser la partie gauche au-dessus et sous les autres parties et placer dans une pince séparation mèches Patrick Cameron

Step 9
- Technik wiederholen
- Ripetere gli stessi passaggi
- Repetir la técnica
- Répéter la technique

Step 12
- Die letzten Enden kreuzweise nehmen und mit Haarspangen befestigen
- Incrociare le code finali e fermare con le clip
- Entrecruzar las colas finales y sujetar con pinzas de peluquería
- Entrecroiser les dernières queues et placer avec des pinces séparation mèches

Step 14
- Enden lösen und beide Seiten nach oben drehen
- Liberare le code e intrecciare i due lati verso l'alto
- Soltar las colas y enrollar hacia arriba ambos lados
- Relâcher les queues et torsader les deux côtés vers le haut

Step 16
- Rechte Seite mit einer Patrick Cameron-Haarspange festhalten und links am Kopf befestigen
- Trattenere la parte a destra una clip Patrick Cameron e fermare con una forcina la parte a sinistra
- Sujetar el lado derecho con un pinza de peluquería Patrick Cameron y el izquierdo al cuero cabelludo
- Maintenir le côté droit avec une pince séparation mèches Patrick Cameron et fixer à gauche sur le cuir chevelu

Step 17
- Mit Enden (Tails) schmücken
- Decorare con le code
- Decorar con colas
- Décorer avec des queues

Step 19
- Auf der gegenüberliegenden Seite wiederholen
- Ripetere sul lato opposto
- Repetir en el otro lado
- Répéter le mouvement du côté opposé

Step 20
- Den oberen hinteren Teil in einer Welle drapieren, Spray auftragen und mit Diffuser trocknen
- Modellare la parte superiore in un'onda, rifinire con spray e diffusore
- Disponer la parte superior trasera en una onda, aplicar spray y secar con difusor
- Draper le haut à l'arrière en ondulation, laquer et sécher au diffuseur

Step 21
- Die Welle mit einer geschlossenen Haarklemme quer über dem Kopf feststecken
- Fermare l'onda con una forcina chiusa
- Sujetar la onda con una horquilla cerrada en la cabeza
- Fixer la vague en plaçant une barrette en travers de la tête

Step 22
- Mit Patrick Cameron Accessoires schmücken
- Decorare con gli accessori Patrick Cameron
- Decorar con accesorios Patrick Cameron
- Décorer avec des accessoires Patrick Cameron

Stephanie style 3

Create triangular section

Create right side section

Hot roller and section clip to hold

Take another 2cm wide section and twist to right

Stephanie style 3

5

Take back section under and over

6

Twist both together firmly to scalp

<u>Tip</u>
Twist must be tight.
Always twist in
the same
direction

7

Pull twist around to front,
taking a front section over
and under twist

8

Continue twisting firmly to
scalp, creating a roped figure
8 effect

Stephanie style 3

9

10

11

Continue down head

12

Grip at neck

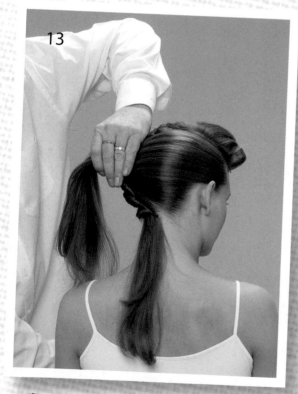

13

Brush firmly over to roping

14

Grip to hold

Stephanie style 3

Split into two and twist firmly

Allow twist to figure 8 over grips and grip to hold

Repeat twist

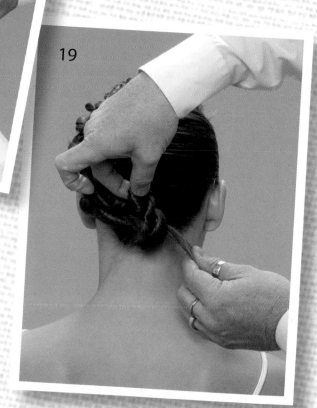

Twist tail up and grip

Stephanie style 3

20

21

Drape front into soft wave

Decorate with Patrick Cameron accessories

Product:
*Use SP Pearl Smooth
to add shine
and hold*

Step 1
- Auf der rechten Seite eine Haarpartie abteilen
- Creare una sezione sul lato destro
- Crear una sección en el lateral derecho
- Créer une partie côté droit

Step 2
- Eine dreieckige Haarpartie abteilen
- Creare una sezione triangolare
- Crear una sección triangular
- Créer une partie triangulaire

Step 3
- Große Rolle (Hot Roller) und Haarclip, um Halt zu geben
- Bigodini riscaldanti e clip per fissare
- Utilizar rulos calientes y pinzas de peluquería para sujetar
- Mettre des bigoudis chauffants et fixer avec des pinces séparation mèches pour maintenir

Step 4
- Eine weitere 2 cm breite Haarpartie nehmen und nach rechts drehen
- Prendere un'altra sezione di 2 cm e attorcigliarla sulla destra
- Tomar otra sección de 2cm de ancho y enrollar hacia la derecha
- Prendre une autre partie de 2cm de large et torsader vers la droite

Step 5
- Die hintere Haarpartie darunter und darüber legen

Step 5 (continued)
- Portare la sezione posteriore sotto l'altra sezione e ricoprirla
- Llevar la sección posterior por debajo y por encima
- Reprendre la partie dessous et dessus

Step 6
- Beide fest zusammen bis zum Kopf drehen
- Attorcigliare entrambe le sezioni fino alla radice
- Enrollar ambas secciones juntas y sujetarlas firmemente al cuero cabelludo
- Torsader fermement les deux parties ensemble au cuir chevelu

Step 7
- Das geht regte Haar den Kopf herum nach vorne ziehen, dabei eine Haarpartie von vorne über und unter die gedrehte Haarpartie legen
- Tirare la ciocca attorcigliata sul davanti, prendendo una sezione anteriore sopra e sotto la ciocca stessa
- Tirar del cabello enrollado hacia delante, llevando una sección frontal por encima y por debajo del cabello enrollado
- Tirer la torsade autour du dessus, prendre une partie avant dessus et sous la torsade

Step 8
- Weiter fest bis zum Kopf drehen, so dass im Effekt eine geflochtene "8" entsteht
- Continuare a attorcigliare, creando un effetto "a fune"
- Seguir enrollando y sujetando firmemente al cuero cabelludo, creando un efecto de cuerda en 8.
- Continuer à torsader fermement au cuir chevelu, en créant un 8 tressé

Step 9
- Auf diese Weise weiter den Kopf hinunter vorgehen
- Continuare verso il basso
- Seguir bajando por la cabeza
- Continuer en bas de la tête

Step 11
- Im Nacken mit Klammer befestigen
- Fissare sul collo
- Sujetar al cuello
- Fixer au niveau du cou

Step 13
- Fest darüber bürsten bis zum geflochtenen Teil
- Spazzolare
- Cepillar firmemente sobre el cabello enrollado
- Brosser fermement au-dessus de la tresse

Step 14
- Mit Klammer befestigen, um Halt zu geben
- Fermare con una forcina
- Sujetar con horquillas
- Fixer pour maintenir en place

Step 15
- In zwei Teile unterteilen und fest drehen
- Dividere in due e attorcigliare
- Dividir en dos y enrollar firmemente
- Partager en deux et torsader solidement

Step 16
- So drehen, dass über Haarklammern eine "8" entsteht und mit Klammer befestigen, um Halt zu geben

Step 9 (continued)
- Avvolgere la ciocca attorcigliata a forma di 8 fissandola con le forcine
- Colocar el cabello enrollado en 8 por encima de las horquillas y sujetar
- Faire un 8 avec la tresse au-dessus des fixe-mèches et fixer pour maintenir en place

Step 17
- Drehen wiederholen
- Ripetere il passaggio
- Repetir el proceso de enrollado
- Répéter la torsade

Step 19
- Ende nach oben drehen und mit Klammer befestigen
- Avvolgere verso l'alto e fissare
- Enrollar la cola hacia arriba y sujetarla
- Entortiller la queue dessus et fixer

Step 20
- Das Haar vorne zu einer sanften Welle drapieren
- Modellare sul davanti in un'onda morbida
- Disponer la parte frontal en una onda suave
- Draper le devant en une vague souple

Step 21
- Mit Patrick Cameron Accessoires schmücken
- Decorare con gli accessori Patrick Cameron
- Decorar con accesorios Patrick Cameron
- Décorer avec des accessoires Patrick Cameron

Stephanie style 3

Gergana style 3

Section temple to temple and behind crown

Use fingers to pull back softly into ponytail

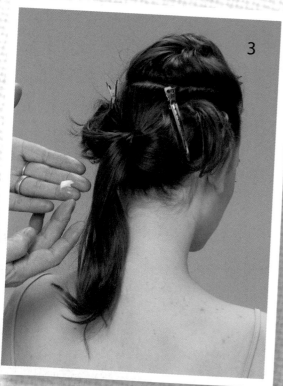

Divide ponytail into 3 sections

Tip

Hair preparation – Soft round brush blow dry or loose hot roller set

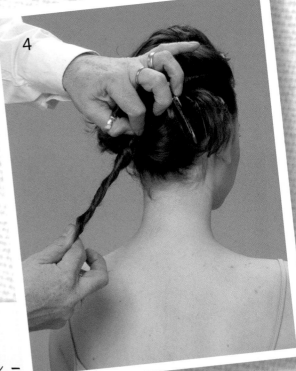

Twist softly

Gergana style 3

5

Pull gently to create texture

6

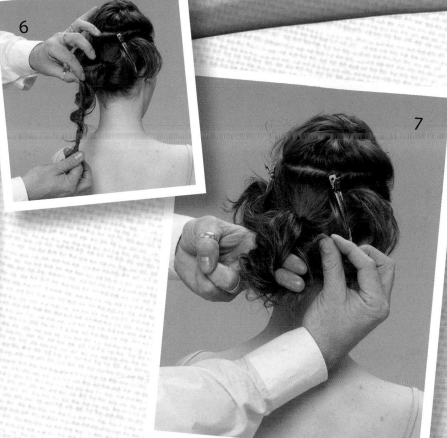

7

Create loose barrel curl

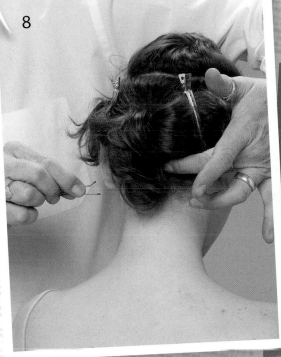

8

Grip to hold

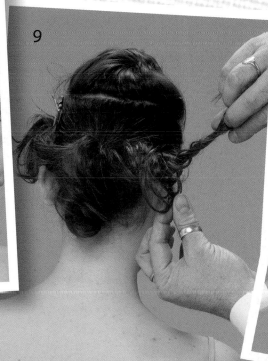

9

10

Repeat

Product:
Use SP Pearl Smooth
to add shine
and hold

Gergana style 3

Backcomb gently to roots

Barrel curl tails gently back behind crown

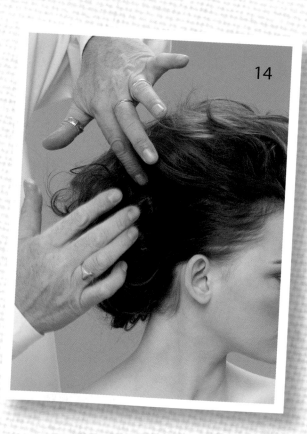

Step 1
- Eine Haarpartie von Schläfe zu Schläfe und hinter dem Oberkopf
- Sezione tra le due tempie e dietro la corona
- Dividir el cabello de sien a sien y detrás de la coronilla
- Partie tempe à tempe et derrière le dessus de tête

Step 2
- Nehmen Sie die Finger, um das Haar sanft nach hinten zu einem Pferdeschwanz zu ziehen
- Pettinare con le dita per formare una coda morbida
- Utilizar los dedos para llevar hacia atrás suavemente y hacer una coleta
- Utiliser les doigts pour tirer doucement dans la queue de cheval

Step 3
- Den Pferdeschwanz in 3 Haarpartien unterteilen
- Dividere la coda in 3 sezioni
- Dividir la coleta en 3 secciones
- Séparer la queue de cheval en 3

Step 4
- Sanft drehen
- Attorcigliare leggermente
- Enrollar suavemente
- Torsader souplement

Step 5
- Leicht ziehen, so dass eine Textur entsteht
- Pizzicare delicatamente per creare texture
- Tirar suavemente para crear textura
- Tirer doucement pour créer la texture

Step 7
- Eine lockere Barrel-Locke legen
- Creare un boccolo morbido
- Crear unas ondas sueltas
- Créer une grosse boucle souple

Step 8
- Mit Klammer befestigen, um Halt zu geben
- Fermare con una forcina
- Sujetar con horquillas
- Fixer pour maintenir en place

Step 9
- Wiederholen
- Ripetere
- Repetir
- Répéter le mouvement

Step 11
- Leicht bis zum Haaransatz toupieren
- Cotonare delicatamente le radici
- Cardar suavemente hasta la raíz
- Crêper légèrement aux racines

Step 13
- Die Enden hinter dem Oberkopf leicht nach hinten zu Barrel-Locken drapieren
- Portare le code a boccolo dietro la corona della testa.
- Crear ondas en las colas llevándolas suavemente hacia atrás por detrás de la coronilla
- La grande boucle tombe souplement derrière le dessus de tête

Gergana style 3

Ella style 3

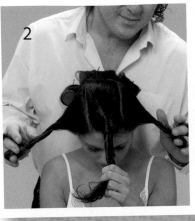

Leave soft section at front and grip the rest back at crown

Wrap tail around a Patrick Cameron hair pad

Tip

Fit hair pad shape just below crown to allow style to sit back, not too high on the head.

Grip to hold

Ella style 3

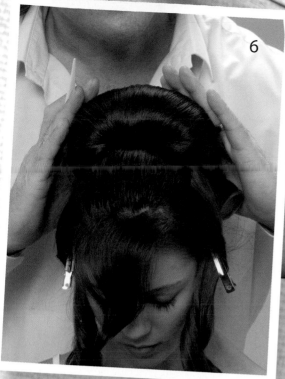

Create crescent shape and spread hair evenly over shape

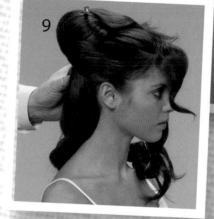

Brush sides back on 45 degree angle up and over pad

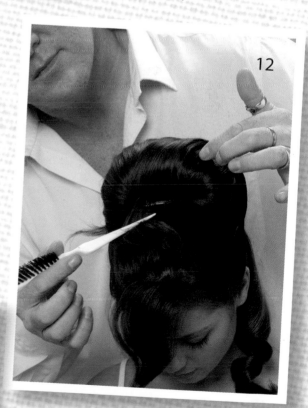

Repeat on opposite side

Grip tails to base

Ella style 3

103

13

Cover grips with remaining tails

14

Decorate with Patrick Cameron accessories

15

16

Fit veil under roll

Tip
See veil technique for fitting

Step 3
- Eine weiche Partie vorne belassen und den Rest hinten am Oberkopf feststecken
- Separare una sezione morbida sul davanti e fermare i capelli sotto la corona
- Dejar una sección suelta en el frente y sujetar el resto detrás en la coronilla
- Laisser la partie de devant souple et fixer le reste de la chevelure à l'arrière du dessus de tête

Step 4
- Ende um ein Patrick Cameron Hair Pad wickeln
- Avvolgere la coda intorno a un crespo Patrick Cameron
- Enrollar la cola alrededor de un postizo Patrick Cameron
- Enrouler la queue autour d'un boudin Patrick Cameron

Step 5
- Mit einer Haarklammer befestigten
- Fermare con una forcina
- Sujetar con horquillas
- Fixer pour maintenir en place

Step 6
- Das Haar sichelförmig anlegen und gleichmäßig in die Form einbeziehen

- Creare una forma a mezzaluna e distribuire uniformemente i capelli su questa forma
- Crear una forma de media luna y distribuir el cabello uniformemente sobre la forma
- Créer une forme en croissant et étaler les cheveux de manière régulière au-dessus de la forme

Step 8
- Die Seiten nach hinten in einem 45° Winkel hoch und über das Pad bürsten
- Spazzolare i lati di 45 gradi verso l'alto ricoprendo il crespo
- Cepillar los lados hacia atrás en un ángulo de 45 grados hacia arriba y sobre el postizo
- Brosser les côtés à l'arrière dans un angle à 45 degrés vers le haut et sur le boudin

Step 10
- Auf der gegenüberliegenden Seite wiederholen
- Ripetere sul lato opposto
- Repetir en el otro lado
- Répéter le mouvement du côté opposé

Step 12
- Enden am Ansatz mit Klammern befestigen
- Fermare le code alla base
- Sujetar las colas a la base

- Saisir les queues à la base

Step 13
- Haarklammern mit den übrig gebliebenen Enden verdecken
- Coprire le forcine con le code rimanenti
- Tapar las horquillas con las colas restantes
- Recouvrir les fixe-mèches avec les autres queues

Step 14
- Vordere Kopfpartie stylen
- Pettinare la sezione sul davanti
- Peinar la parte frontal
- Coiffer le devant

Step15
- Mit Patrick Cameron Accessoires schmücken
- Decorare con gli accessori Patrick Cameron
- Decorar con accesorios Patrick Cameron
- Décorer avec des accessoires Patrick Cameron

Step16
- Schleier unter der Rolle befestigen
- Inserire il velo sotto l'acconciatura
- Colocar el velo bajo el rodete
- Fixer le voile sous le rouleau

Ella style 3

FUSE THE ELIXIRS OF
CARE FOR PERSONALIZED
HAIR PERFECTION.

System Professional's new Infusion range places advanced hair science in your hands. Mix care benefits to craft perfection: fuse polished smoothness with ultimate repair for a new level of personalized hair care. www.wella.com

SP. THE SCIENCE OF PERSONALIZED CARE. FROM **WELLA** PROFESSIONALS

Patrick Cameron has justly earned his place in hairdressing's hall of fame as one of the world's leading platform artists, giving him the title, 'The Maestro of Long Hair'.

A regular on television screens both in the UK and overseas and appearing at the most prestigious global hairdressing events all over the world, Patrick continues to educate and inspire many with his visual and often avant garde stage productions. Using his skills gained whilst working as a salon stylist and platform artist, he combines the commercial aspects of speed required for salon work with the theatrical, which enthralls his audiences.

Taking his inspiration from an eclectic variety of sources, Patrick has year after year grabbed the hairdressing headlines when presenting his innovative collections.

In addition to his global appearances and London based Training School, Patrick always takes time out of his busy schedule to visit at least five UK colleges each year where he will present Look and Learn seminars to eager young students, many of whom otherwise would not get the chance to see him demonstrate and present his many talents.

Patrick's philosophy is one that has taken him around the world many times and is one that translates well into any language. "My aim is to create natural looks that make women feel feminine," says Patrick. "When I am presenting on stage I try to break down my techniques into simple step by step instructions so that my audiences can go away and think 'I can do that'. If they leave the show feeling like that, then I have done my job"

Patrick's zest, energy, vitality and dedication to his craft seem never ending. One of the most charming and talented people you could ever meet, Patrick has justly earned his title, "The Maestro of Long Hair'.

For further information about Patrick Cameron Limited, please contact his business partner:
Sue Callaghan, Patrick Cameron Limited, The Paddocks, Woodbank Lane, Woodbank, Chester CH1 6JD, United Kingdom
Tel: +44 (0) 1244 880807   Fax: +44 (0) 1244 881140   email: sue@patrick-cameron.com

"Breakfast at Tiffany's"
1996

"Tango"
1997

"Queen"
1998

"Global Tribe"
1999

"Arts and Crafts"
2000

"Nightlife"
2001

"Visionaire"
2002

"Bohemian Revolution"
2003

"Provocateur"
2004

"Cream"
2005

"Ladies Who Lunch"
2006

"Pure"
2007

"Red Carpet"
2008

"Prestige"
2009

"Gold"
2010

Patrick Cameron in Action

*i*n 1997 Patrick Cameron opened his own training school to give students intensive tuition in the art of dressing long hair. Courses take place in London and around the world on a regular basis under Patrick's personal guidance and supervision.

"I like to teach students just one or two steps at a time to break down the style into a logical, easy to understand structure," says Patrick. "Usually we cover at least four styles a day and the results, using this method with small groups of students is superb. My students have ranged from newly qualified hairdressers keen to come to grips with long hair, to experienced professionals looking for further inspiration. The exclusive nature of this course allows me to concentrate on each person's individual needs."

*1*997 eröffnete Patrick Cameron seine eigene Friseurschule, in der er seinen Studenten und Studentinnen die Frisierkunst an langem Haar zeigt. Die Kurse finden regelmäßig in London und rund um den Globus unter Patricks persönlicher Fuhrung und Aufsicht statt.

„Ich zeige meinen Studenten jeweils nur ein, zwei Schritte, damit sie die logische, leicht verständliche Struktur der Frisur begreifen", so Patrick. „Normalerweise bringen wir unseren Studenten mindestens vier verschiedene Frisuren pro Tag bei. Glauben Sie mir, mit dieser Methode mit kleinen Studiengruppen lassen sich die Ergebnisse wirklich sehen! Zu mir kommen Fiseure, die ihren Abschluss gerade erst in der Tasche haben und wissen mochten, wie sie am besten mit langen Haaren umgehen, aber auch Friseure mit langjähriger Erfahrung, die neue Anregungen suchen. Der Kurs ist so aufgebaut, dass ich mich ganz nach den Wünschen der einzelnen Teilnehmer richten kann."

*n*el 1997 Patrick Cameron decise di aprire una scuola dedicata esclusivamente all'arte della acconciatura raccolta. I corsi si tengono a Londra dove Patrick risiede e a volte in trasferta in altri paesi del mondo sempre sotto la guida e supervisione personale di Patrick.

"Mi piace dimostrare agli studenti uno o due passaggi alla volta per spiegare il look in modo logico e facile da comprendere," dice Patrick. "Di solito realizziamo un minimo di quattro stili al giorno, e i risultati quando si ha un numero ridotto di studenti sono straordinari. Fra i partecipanti ci sono sia parrucchieri appena qualificati che desiderano lavorare con i capelli lunghi che professionisti esperti alla ricerca di nuove idee. La natura esclusiva di questo corso mi consente di concentrarmi sulle esigenze di ogni persona."

*e*n 1997, Patrick Cameron abrió su propia escuela para ofrecer a los estudiantes formación intensiva en el arte de peinar el cabello largo. Los cursos tienen lugar en Londres y en otras partes del mundo con regularidad bajo la supervisión y el asesoramiento personal de Patrick.

"Me gusta enseñar a los alumnos uno o dos pasos a la vez, para desglosar el peinado en una estructura lógica y fácil de comprender", explica Patrick. "Normalmente cubrimos como mínimo cuatro peinados al día, y los resultados de utilizar este metódo con grupos reducidos de estudiantes son excelentes. Entre mis alumnos se cuentan desde peluqueros que acaban de obtener el título, ansiosos por aprender a tratar el pelo largo, hasta profesionales expertos que buscan nueva inspiración. La naturaleza exclusiva de este curso me permite concentrarme en las necesidades individuales de cada persona."

*e*n 1997, Patrick Cameron ouvrit sa propre école de formation pour donner aux étudiants des cours intensifs dans l'art de coiffer les cheveux longs. Les cours ont lieu régulièrement à Londres et partout dans le monde sous la direction et la supervision personnelles de Patrick. «J'aime enseigner aux étudiants une ou deux étapes à la fois pour décomposer le style en une structure logique facile à comprendre» raconte Patrick: «D'habitude, nous couvrons 4 styles par jour et les résultats obtenus, après avoir utilisé cette méthode en petits groupes d'étudiants, sont brillants. Mes étudiants comprenaient des coiffeurs nouvellement diplômés impatients d'arriver aux pinces avec des longs cheveux pour faire l'expérience des looks professionnels afin de s'en inspirer pour l'avenir. La nature exclusive de ce cours me permet de me concentrer sur les besoins de chaque individu.»

For further information on the Patrick Cameron Training School and merchandising items, please vist our website at:
www.patrick-cameron.com
or contact Studio Manager Marco Everard, Patrick Cameron Limited, 30 Aden Grove, London N16 9NJ, United Kingdom
Tel/Fax: +44 (0) 20 7923 0599 email: marco@patrick-cameron.com

Training School

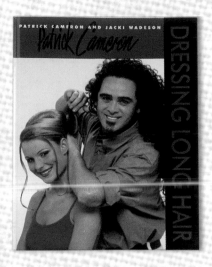

Patrick Cameron: Dressing Long Hair

Patrick's first book is a timeless classic. Featuring over 30 different long hair designs and techniques.

- A magical mix of twists, weaves, curls and braids.
- Over 450 full colour photographs.
- Detailed instructions and professional tips on styling and dressing long hair.

Patrick Cameron: Dressing Long Hair Book 2

- 15 step-by-step long hair styles
- Hundreds of detailed step-by-step photographs.
- Imaginative format of fold out pages to view at a glance

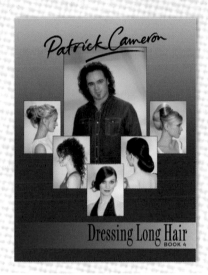

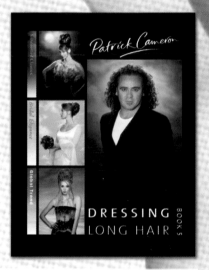

**Patrick Cameron:
Dressing Long Hair Book 3**

**Patrick Cameron:
Dressing Long Hair Book 4**

**Patrick Cameron:
Dressing Long Hair Book 5**

Each book contains 15 stunning themed step-by-step long hair styles, illustrated with hundreds of detailed step-by-step photographs.

Long Awaited DVD
Patrick's 3 'Long Awaited' videos, now on DVD, featuring 18 styles

How to Dress Long Hair DVD
The Bridal Collection parts 1 & 2 featuring 12 original styles

The Show Collection DVD
3 stunning shows featuring new and original styles

Pure DVD
Brand new styles created by Patrick for Bridal Hair

Red Carpet & Prestige DVD
2 collections of inspirational styles on 1 DVD

For further information on the Patrick Cameron Training School and merchandising items, please vist our website at:
www.patrick-cameron.com
or contact Studio Manager Marco Everard, Patrick Cameron Limited, 30 Aden Grove, London N16 9NJ, United Kingdom
Tel/Fax: +44 (0) 20 7923 0599 email: marco@patrick-cameron.com

Books and DVDs

Long hair pack

Long hair styling brush

Human hair wefts

Hair ties

Section clips

Synthetic hair pads

Hair accessories

End elastics

Hair	Photography	Make-up	Clothes styling and digital retouching	Hair styling products	Hair styling equipment
PATRICK CAMERON	Alistair Hughes	Alison Chesterton	Marco Erbi	System Professional	Babyliss Pro

With thanks to

Marco Everard · Sue Callaghan · Alexander Herzberg · Debora Guizzo · Angela Vivado · Tim Heldmann · Paul Jones
Will White · Maureen Barrymore · Phil Ollerenshaw

First published 2009 by Patrick Cameron Limited, 30 Aden Grove, London N16 9NJ, United Kingdom.

ISBN 9780954110635

Designed by Umbrella Communications   Printed by LEGO SpA

Merchandising and Acknowledgments